Study Guide and Workbook

LYNN FLEISCHMAN
MARK L. BERENSON
DAVID M. LEVINE
MABEL YU

Department of Statistics and Computer Information Systems
Baruch College, City University of New York

Basic Business Statistics THIRD EDITION
CONCEPTS AND APPLICATIONS

MARK L. BERENSON
DAVID M. LEVINE

PRENTICE-HALL, INC., ENGLEWOOD CLIFFS, NEW JERSEY 07632

Editorial/production supervision: Linda Marie Scardelis
Cover design: Paul Silverman
Manufacturing buyer: Ed O'Dougherty

Printed in the United States of America

10 9 8 7 6 5 4 3 2 1

ISBN: 0-13-057761-8   01

Prentice-Hall International (UK) Limited, London
Prentice-Hall of Australia Pty. Limited, Sydney
Prentice-Hall Canada Inc., Toronto
Prentice-Hall Hispanoamericana, S.A., Mexico
Prentice-Hall of India Private Limited, New Delhi
Prentice-Hall of Japan, Inc., Tokyo
Prentice-Hall of Southeast Asia Pte. Ltd., Singapore
Editora Prentice-Hall do Brasil, Ltda., Rio de Janeiro
Whitehall Books Limited, Wellington, New Zealand

Contents

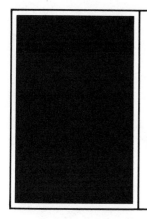

Preface

The most productive way to learn applied statistical methods is to work out various types of problems as a means of understanding the concepts and methodology involved. The major function of this Study Guide is to provide such examples.

We have written the Study Guide as a supplement to Basic Business Statistics: Concepts and Applications. Each chapter contains several parts. First, the basic concepts covered in the chapter are summarized. This is followed by multiple choice questions (the answers to which are provided in the back of the guide). Next, several examples using the techniques and concepts of the chapter are presented along with their solutions. Finally, review problems for the chapter are given for the student to solve, followed by their solutions.

The Study Guide also contains a review of arithmetic and algebra that will be particularly useful to those students with limited exposure to mathematics courses since high school. A diagnostic quiz is provided along with the solutions so the student is made aware of any deficiencies. This appendix will enable the student to focus on the concepts of statistics rather than the mechanics of obtaining solutions.

The authors wish to express their thanks to Ms. Ann J. Festa for typing the Study Guide as well as for her editorial assistance.

Lynn Fleischman
Mark Berenson
David Levine
Mabel Yu

1 Introduction

The subject of statistics encompasses all fields of application from Anthropology to Zoology. Statistical information of all types in all fields is being continually collected, processed, analyzed, and utilized for the purpose of making rational decisions. Chapter 1 focuses on the growth of the subject of statistics and presents several illustrations indicating statistical applications. Such concepts as population versus sample, parameter versus statistic, and statistical description versus statistical inference are considered.

MULTIPLE CHOICE

1. The process of using sample statistics to draw conclusions about the true population parameters is called

   (a) statistical inference.
   (b) the scientific method.
   (c) sampling.
   (d) descriptive statistics.

2. Those methods involving the collection, summarization, presentation, and characterization of a set of data in order to properly describe the various features of that set of data are called

   (a) statistical inference.
   (b) the scientific method.
   (c) sampling.
   (d) descriptive statistics.

3. The universe or "totality of items or things" under consideration in a statistical study is

   (a) a sample.
   (b) a population.
   (c) a parameter.
   (d) a statistic.

4. The portion of the universe that has been selected for analysis in a statistical study is

   (a) a sample.
   (b) a population.
   (c) a parameter.
   (d) a statistic.

5. A summary measure that is computed to describe a characteristic from only a sample of the population is called

   (a) a parameter.
   (b) the random generator.
   (c) a statistic.
   (d) the scientific method.

6. A summary measure that is computed to describe a characteristic of an entire population is called

   (a) a parameter.
   (b) the random generator.
   (c) a statistic.
   (d) the scientific method.

7. The increased use of statistical methods in recent years is <u>primarily</u> due to

   (a) scientific exploration.
   (b) mathematical inquisitiveness.
   (c) the accessibility of high-speed digital computers.
   (d) increased interest in gambling.

2

2 Data Collection

Proper data collection is a most important phase of any research endeavor. Therefore, this chapter examines different types of data, considers different sources of data and, in particular, focuses on the art of questionnaire development and various sampling methods. In addition, problems with respect to coding, editing, and data entry are discussed.

MULTIPLE CHOICE

1. Brand preference for television sets is an example of a

   (a) discrete variable.
   (b) continuous variable.
   (c) qualitative variable.
   (d) constant.

2. Number of days in the month of June is an example of a

   (a) discrete variable.
   (b) continuous variable.
   (c) qualitative variable.
   (d) constant.

3. Flight time from New York City to Denver is an example of a

   (a) discrete variable.
   (b) continuous variable.
   (c) qualitative variable.
   (d) constant.

4. A table of random numbers is primarily used to

(a) compute probabilities.
(b) assure the selection of a random sample.
(c) set up frequency distribution tables.
(d) minimize errors of nonresponse.

5. A sample of 400 subscribers to a particular magazine is selected from a population listing of 8,000 subscribers. If, upon examining the data, it is determined that no subscriber has been selected in the sample more than once

(a) the sample could not have been random.
(b) the sample may have been selected without replacement or with replacement.
(c) the sample had to have been selected with replacement.
(d) the sample had to have been selected without replacement.

6. Which of the following statements regarding nonprobability samples is not true?

(a) They are usually less costly than probability samples.
(b) They are usually less laborious than probability samples.
(c) They are usually more convenient than probability samples.
(d) They are usually more accurate then probability samples.

7. Which of the following types of samples is a probability sample?

(a) The chunk.
(b) The cluster sample.
(c) The judgment sample.
(d) The quota sample.

8. For a population list containing N = 1,001 individuals, what code number would you assign to the first person on the list in order to use a table of random numbers (Table E.1)?

(a) 0
(b) 1
(c) 01
(d) 0001

EXAMPLE

I. State the level of measurement for the following:

(a) The classification of social classes as working, middle, and upper.
(b) The measure of physical distances, i.e., feet or meters.
(c) The country in which you were born.
(d) The Fahrenheit and Centigrade systems.

SOLUTION

(a) Ordinal-level measurement.
(b) Ratio-level measurement.
(c) Nominal-level measurement.
(d) Interval-level measurement.

Supplement

Summation Notation

The symbol "Σ" means the "summation of". Thus

$$\sum_{i=1}^{n} X_i = X_1 + X_2 + X_3 + \ldots + X_n$$

$$\sum_{i=1}^{n} X_i^2 = X_1^2 + X_2^2 + \ldots + X_n^2$$

and

$$\sum_{i=1}^{n} X_i Y_i = X_1 Y_1 + X_2 Y_2 + \ldots + X_n Y_n$$

Rules of Summation:

Rule 1. $\displaystyle\sum_{i=1}^{n} (X_i + Y_i) = \sum_{i=1}^{n} X_i + \sum_{i=1}^{n} Y_i$

Rule 2. $\displaystyle\sum_{i=1}^{n} (X_i - Y_i) = \sum_{i=1}^{n} X_i - \sum_{i=1}^{n} Y_i$

Rule 3. $\displaystyle\sum_{i=1}^{n} C X_i = C \sum_{i=1}^{n} X_i$

Rule 4. $\displaystyle\sum_{i=1}^{n} C = nC$

The application of the four summation rules provides us with a means of simplifying complex algebraic expressions so that ultimately numerical computations are facilitated.

EXAMPLE

Simplify algebraically and solve numerically the following expression:

$$\sum_{i=1}^{n} (X_i + 5Y_i^2 - C)$$

where

$$\sum_{i=1}^{n} X_i = 100 \qquad \sum_{i=1}^{n} Y_i^2 = 60 \qquad C = 90 \qquad n = 4$$

SOLUTION

Using Summation Rules 1 and 2 we have

$$\sum_{i=1}^{n} (X_i + 5Y_i^2 - C) = \sum_{i=1}^{n} X_i + \sum_{i=1}^{n} 5Y_i^2 - \sum_{i=1}^{n} C$$

Using Summation Rule 3 we have

$$\sum_{i=1}^{n} X_i + \sum_{i=1}^{n} 5Y_i^2 - \sum_{i=1}^{n} C = \sum_{i=1}^{n} X_i + 5\sum_{i=1}^{n} Y_i^2 - \sum_{i=1}^{n} C$$

Using Summation Rule 4 we have

$$\sum_{i=1}^{n} X_i + 5\sum_{i=1}^{n} Y_i^2 - \sum_{i=1}^{n} C = \sum_{i=1}^{n} X_i + 5\sum_{i=1}^{n} Y_i^2 - nC$$

and the latter expression is the algebraic simplification. Now to solve numerically, we merely substitute the given information and the following result is obtained:

$$\sum_{i=1}^{n} (X_i + 5Y_i^2 - C) = \sum_{i=1}^{n} X_i + 5\sum_{i=1}^{n} Y_i^2 - nC$$

$$= 100 + (5)(60) - (4)(90) = 40.$$

REVIEW PROBLEM

Simplify algebraically and solve numerically the following expression:

$$\sum_{i=1}^{n} (X_i^2 + CY_i + 4X_iY_i - 50)$$

where

$$X_1 = 1 \qquad X_2 = 10 \qquad X_3 = 4 \qquad n = 3$$

$$Y_1 = 2 \qquad Y_2 = 1 \qquad Y_3 = 5 \qquad C = 5$$

SOLUTION TO REVIEW PROBLEM

$$\sum_{i=1}^{n} (X_i^2 + CY_i + 4X_iY_i - 50) = \sum_{i=1}^{n} X_i^2 + \sum_{i=1}^{n} CY_i + \sum_{i=1}^{n} 4X_iY_i - \sum_{i=1}^{n} 50 \qquad \text{(Rules 1 \& 2)}$$

$$= \sum_{i=1}^{n} X_i^2 + C \sum_{i=1}^{n} Y_i + 4 \sum_{i=1}^{n} X_iY_i - \sum_{i=1}^{n} 50 \qquad \text{(Rule 3)}$$

$$= \sum_{i=1}^{n} X_i^2 + C \sum_{i=1}^{n} Y_i + 4 \sum_{i=1}^{n} X_iY_i - 50n \qquad \text{(Rule 4)}$$

The latter expression is the algebraic simplification. The numerical result is obtained by substitution as follows:

$$\sum_{i=1}^{n} X_i^2 + C \sum_{i=1}^{n} Y_i + 4 \sum_{i=1}^{n} X_iY_i - 50n$$

Since

$$\sum_{i=1}^{n} X_i^2 = (1)(1) + (10)(10) + (4)(4) = \mathbf{117}$$

we have

$$\sum_{i=1}^{n} Y_i = 2 + 1 + 5 = 8$$

and

$$\sum_{i=1}^{n} X_iY_i = (1)(2) + (10)(1) + (4)(5) = 32$$

Thus,

$$\sum_{i=1}^{n} X_i^2 + C \sum_{i=1}^{n} Y_i + 4 \sum_{i=1}^{n} X_iY_i - 50n = (117) + (5)(8) + (4)(32) - (50)(3)$$

$$= 135.$$

3

Describing and Summarizing Data

Once quantitative data have been collected, proper analysis and interpretation are essential. Data have three major properties or characteristics-- central tendency, dispersion, and shape. A variety of descriptive summary measures representing these properties may be used to extract and summarize the salient features of the data set. This chapter focuses on the conceptual development, computation, and use of such descriptive measures for data collected in their raw form (ungrouped data).

MULTIPLE CHOICE

1. In a right-skewed distribution

   (a) the median equals the mean.
   (b) the mean is less than the median.
   (c) the mean is greater than the mode.
   (d) the median is less than the mode.

2. Which of the following measures of variability is not dependent on the exact value of each observation?

   (a) range
   (b) variance
   (c) standard deviation
   (d) coefficient of variation

3. Which of the following statements about the mean is not necessarily true?

   (a) It is greatly affected by extreme values.
   (b) It is the point about which the summed deviations is zero.
   (c) It is the point about which the sum of squared deviations is a minimum total.
   (d) It is the point about which the sum of absolute deviations is a minimum total.

4. According to the Bienaymé-Chebyshev rule, at least _____ percent of the observations in a sample are contained within $\pm$ 1.5 standard deviations around the mean--regardless of the shape of the distribution.

   (a) 75.0   (c) 33.3
   (b) 55.6   (d) 0.0

5. When extreme values are present in the data the following descriptive measures are useful:

   (a) CV and range.   (c) mode and median.
   (b) $\bar{X}$ and S.   (d) S^2 and interquartile range.

6. For any set of measurements, what is the sum of the deviations of the measurements from their mean?

   (a) minimum value   (c) 0
   (b) 1   (d) One must see the data.

7. A set of measurements is symmetrical and the median is 4. If there are 1,000 measurements, can you calculate their sum?

   (a) 444   (c) 4,000
   (b) 4,444   (d) It is impossible to calculate their sum.

8. Using the rules for summation, $\sum\limits_{i=1}^{n} (3X_i + C) =$

   (a) $3 \sum\limits_{i=1}^{n} X_i + nC$ (c) $3 \sum\limits_{i=1}^{n} X_i + C$

   (b) $\sum\limits_{i=1}^{n} 3X_i + \sum\limits_{i=1}^{n} C$ (d) $\sum\limits_{i=1}^{n} 3X_i + nC$

EXAMPLE

(Ungrouped Data Calculations)

I. A random sample of 11 vouchers is taken from a corporate expense account. The voucher amounts are as follows:

$276.72	194.17	259.83	249.45
201.43	237.66	199.28	211.49
240.16	261.10	226.21	

A. Compute

    (1) the mean
    (2) the median, Q_1 and Q_3
    (3) the midhinge
    (4) the mode
    (5) the range
    (6) the interquartile range
    (7) the midrange
    (8) the variance (definitional and computational)
    (9) the standard deviation
    (10) the coefficient of variation
    (11) the direction of skewness

B. List the five-number summary.

C. Form the box-and-whisker plot.

D. (1) Using the Bienaymé-Chebyshev rule, between what two values
      would we estimate at least 75% of the vouchers are contained?
    (2) What percentage of the vouchers are actually contained within
      ± 2 standard deviations of the mean?

E. If there were 1,000 vouchers in the corporate expense account, estimate the total value of the corporate expense account.

SOLUTION

A. (1) Computation of the Mean $(\overline{X})$ (2) Computation of the Median,
                                                     Q_1 and Q_3

X_i	Ordered Array
$ 276.72	$ 194.17
201.43	199.28
240.16	201.43 = Q_1
194.17	211.49
237.66	226.21
261.10	237.66 = Median
259.83	240.16
199.28	249.45
226.21	259.83 = Q_3
249.45	261.10
211.49	276.72

$\sum\limits_{i=1}^{11} X_i = \$2,557.50$

Positioning Point Locations:

$\text{Median} = \dfrac{n+1}{2} = \dfrac{11+1}{2} = X_{(6)}$

$\overline{X} = \dfrac{\sum\limits_{i=1}^{n} X_i}{n} = \dfrac{2,557.50}{11} = \$232.50$

$Q_1 = \dfrac{n+1}{4} = \dfrac{11+1}{4} = X_{(3)}$

$Q_3 = \dfrac{3(n+1)}{4} = \dfrac{3(11+1)}{4} = X_{(9)}$

(3) Midhinge = Average of the first and third quartiles = $\dfrac{Q_1 + Q_3}{2}$

11

(4) Midhinge = $\dfrac{201.43 + 259.83}{2} = \dfrac{461.26}{2} = \$230.63$.

(5) Mode = the value that occurs most frequently. There is no mode in this example.

(6) Range = largest value minus smallest value = $X_{(n)} - X_{(1)}$

$$= \$276.72 - 194.17 = \$82.55.$$

(7) Interquartile range = spread of middle 50% of data = $Q_3 - Q_1$

$$= \$259.83 - 201.43 = \$58.40.$$

(8) Midrange = average of smallest and largest values = $\dfrac{X_{(1)} + X_{(n)}}{2}$

$$= \dfrac{194.17 + 276.72}{2} = \dfrac{470.89}{2} = \$235.445.$$

(9) Variance = average squared deviation around the mean.

Definitional formula for variance: $S^2 = \dfrac{\sum\limits_{i=1}^{n} (X_i - \bar{X})^2}{n - 1}$

X_i	$X_i - \bar{X}$	$(X_i - \bar{X})^2$
$ 276.72	276.72 - 232.50 = 44.22	$(44.22)^2$ = 1,955.4084
201.43	201.43 - 232.50 = -31.07	$(-31.07)^2$ = 965.3449
240.16	240.16 - 232.50 = 7.66	$(7.66)^2$ = 58.6756
194.17	194.17 - 232.50 = -38.33	$(-38.33)^2$ = 1,469.1889
237.66	237.66 - 232.50 = 5.16	$(5.16)^2$ = 26.6256
261.10	261.10 - 232.50 = 28.60	$(28.60)^2$ = 817.9600
259.83	259.83 - 232.50 = 27.33	$(27.33)^2$ = 746.9289
199.28	199.28 - 232.50 = -33.22	$(-33.22)^2$ = 1,103.5684
226.21	226.21 - 232.50 = -6.29	$(-6.29)^2$ = 39.5641
249.45	249.45 - 232.50 = 16.95	$(16.95)^2$ = 287.3025
211.49	211.49 - 232.50 = -21.01	$(-21.01)^2$ = 441.4201

$\sum\limits_{i=1}^{11} X_i = \$2,557.50$

$\bar{X} = \$232.50$ $\qquad \sum\limits_{i=1}^{11} (X_i - \bar{X}) = 0 \qquad \sum\limits_{i=1}^{11} (X_i - \bar{X})^2 = 7,911.9874$

$$S^2 = \dfrac{7,911.9874}{11 - 1} = 791.19874 \text{ squared dollars}$$

Computational formula for variance: $S^2 = \dfrac{\sum\limits_{i=1}^{n} X_i^2 - \dfrac{\left(\sum\limits_{i=1}^{n} X_i\right)^2}{n}}{n - 1}$

X_i	X_i^2
$ 276.72	$(276.72)^2$ = 76,573.9584
201.43	$(201.43)^2$ = 40,574.0449
240.16	$(240.16)^2$ = 57,676.8256
194.17	$(194.17)^2$ = 37,701.9889
237.66	$(237.66)^2$ = 56,482.2756
261.10	$(261.10)^2$ = 68,173.2100
259.83	$(259.83)^2$ = 67,511.6289
199.28	$(199.28)^2$ = 39,712.5184
226.21	$(226.21)^2$ = 51,170.9641
249.45	$(249.45)^2$ = 62,225.3025
211.49	$(211.49)^2$ = 44,728.0201

$$\sum_{i=1}^{11} X_i = \$2{,}557.50 \qquad \sum_{i=1}^{11} X_i^2 = 602{,}530.7374$$

$$S^2 = \frac{602{,}530.7374 - \frac{(2557.50)^2}{11}}{10} = \frac{602{,}530.7374 - \frac{6{,}540{,}806.25}{11}}{10} =$$

$$S^2 = \frac{602{,}530.7374 - 594{,}618.75}{10} = \frac{7{,}911.9874}{10} =$$

$$S^2 = 791.19874 \text{ squared dollars.}$$

(10) Standard deviation = square root of the average squared deviation around the mean (i.e., the square root of the variance).

$$S = \sqrt{S^2} = \sqrt{791.19874} = \$28.128.$$

(11) Coefficient of variation - measures dispersion relative to the mean.

$$CV = \frac{S}{\bar{X}} \times 100\% = \frac{28.128}{232.50} \times 100\% = 12.1\%.$$

- (12) Since $\bar{X}$ = \$232.50 < Median = \$237.66, the vouchers appear to be negatively or left skewed.

B. A five-number summary consists of $X_{(1)}$, Q_1, Median, Q_3, and $X_{(n)}$. For our example, the five-number summary is $X_{(1)}$ = \$194.17, Q_1 = \$201.43, Median = \$237.66, Q_3 = \$259.83, and $X_{(n)}$ = \$276.72.

C. The box-and-whisker plot provides a graphical representation of the data based on the five-number summary.

C.

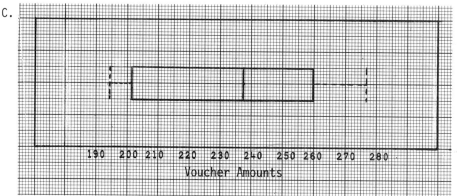

190 200 210 220 230 240 250 260 270 280

Voucher Amounts

BOX-AND-WHISKER PLOT OF VOUCHER AMOUNTS
FROM A CORPORATE EXPENSE ACCOUNT

D. (1) From Bienaymé-Chebyshev rule, at least $(1 - \frac{1}{2^2})$ x 100% = 75.0%
of the observations must be contained within ± 2 standard devia-
tions of the mean (i.e., if $1 - \frac{1}{K^2}$ = .75, then $K = \sqrt{\frac{1}{1 - .75}}$ =
$\sqrt{\frac{1}{.25}}$ = $\sqrt{4}$ = 2). Therefore, at least 75.0% of the voucher
amounts will be between $\bar{X}$ - 2S and $\bar{X}$ + 2S or $232.50 - 2(28.128)
= $176.244 and $232.50 + 2(28.128) = $288.756.

(2) For these data, eleven voucher amounts fall within ± 2 standard
deviations of the mean. Therefore, 100% of the voucher amounts
in this sample are between $176.244 and $288.756.

E. Total value = Population size times the sample mean = $N\bar{X}$.
Total value = 1,000($232.50) = $232,500.

REVIEW PROBLEMS

I. A real-estate agent wants to show apartment seekers rents for unfurnish-
ed studio apartments are higher on the Upper West Side than on the
Upper East Side in New York City. She takes a random sample of nine
studio apartments on the Upper West Side and nine studio apartments on
the Upper East Side. The monthly rents paid are as follows:

Upper West Side	Upper East Side
$297	$267
350	345
273	295
354	335
363	305
321	298
325	350
349	310
347	285

A. For each sample compute:
   (1) the mean

   (2) the median

   (3) the range

   (4) the variance and standard deviation (use computational method)

   (5) the coefficient of variation.

B. If there are 2,000 studio apartments on the Upper West Side and
    2,500 on the Upper East Side, estimate the total monthly rents of
    the two groups of studio apartments if all are rented.

C. Write a brief summary report comparing the monthly rents paid on
    the Upper West Side versus those paid on the Upper East Side.

II. State whether the following are "Possible" or "Impossible."

A. Negative variance.   _Impossible_
B. Mode equal to zero.   _Possible_
C. Positive standard deviation.   _Possible_
D. A set of data with no mode.   _Possible_
E. Variance equal to zero.   _Possible_

SOLUTIONS TO REVIEW PROBLEMS

I. A.

	UPPER WEST SIDE	UPPER EAST SIDE
Ordered Arrays	273 325 350 297 347 354 321 349 363	267 298 335 285 305 345 295 310 350
Sample Size	$n = 9$	$n = 9$
(1) Mean $\bar{X} = \dfrac{\sum\limits_{i=1}^{n} X_i}{n}$	$\sum\limits_{i=1}^{9} X_i = 297 + 350 + \ldots$ $+ 347 = \$2{,}979$ $\bar{X} = \dfrac{\$2{,}979}{9} = \$331.$	$\sum\limits_{i=1}^{9} X_i = 267 + 345 + \ldots$ $+ 285 = \$2{,}790$ $\bar{X} = \dfrac{\$2{,}790}{9} = \$310.$
(2) Median Median = $\dfrac{n+1}{2}$ ordered value	$\dfrac{9+1}{2} = 5\text{th}$ ordered value Median $= X_{(5)} = \$347$	$\dfrac{9+1}{2} = 5\text{th}$ ordered value Median $= X_{(5)} = \$305$
(3) Range Range = $X_{(n)} - X_{(1)}$	$\$363 - 273 = \$90$ Range $= \$90.$	$\$350 - 267 = \$83$ Range $= \$83.$

	UPPER WEST SIDE	UPPER EAST SIDE
(4) Variance		
Computational Formula: $$s^2 = \frac{\sum_{i=1}^{n} X_i^2 - \frac{(\sum_{i=1}^{n} X_i)^2}{n}}{n-1}$$	$$\sum_{i=1}^{9} X_i^2 = 297^2 + 350^2 + \dots + 347^2 = 993,199$$ $$\sum_{i=1}^{9} X_i = 2,979$$ $$s^2 = \frac{993,199 - \frac{(2,979)^2}{9}}{8}$$ $$= \frac{993,199 - 986,049}{8}$$ $$= \frac{7,150}{8} = 893.75$$	$$\sum_{i=1}^{9} X_i^2 = 267^2 + 345^2 + \dots + 285^2 = 871,218$$ $$\sum_{i=1}^{9} X_i = 2,790$$ $$s^2 = \frac{871,218 - \frac{(2,790)^2}{9}}{8}$$ $$= \frac{871,218 - 864,900}{8}$$ $$= \frac{6,318}{8} = 789.75$$
Standard Deviation $$S = \sqrt{S^2}$$	$$S = \sqrt{893.75} = \$29.90$$	$$S = \sqrt{789.75} = \$28.10$$
(5) Coefficient of Variation $$CV = \frac{S}{\bar{X}} \times 100\%$$	$$CV = \frac{29.90}{331} \times 100\%$$ $$= 9.03\%$$	$$CV = \frac{28.10}{310} \times 100\%$$ $$= 9.06\%$$

I. B.

	UPPER WEST SIDE	UPPER EAST SIDE
Mean	$\bar{X} = \$331$	$\bar{X} = \$310$
Standard Deviation	$S = \$29.90$	$S = \$28.10$
Population Size	$N = 2,000$	$N = 2,500$

	UPPER WEST SIDE	UPPER EAST SIDE
Total Total = N$\bar{X}$	Total = 2,000($331) = $662,000	Total = 2,500($310) = $775,000

C.

In terms of central tendency, based on the sample results, the monthly rents on the Upper West Side are higher than those on the Upper East Side. This can be seen by comparing the sample means which describe the average value in a set of data. The mean rent for the Upper West Side is $331 as compared to $310 for the Upper East Side. In addition, the median rent, which is the middle value, is also larger for the Upper West Side ($347) than for the Upper East Side ($305).

In terms of variability, the standard deviation of the monthly rents on the Upper West Side ($29.90) is larger than that on the Upper East Side ($28.10). However, since the difference in the average monthly rents between the two groups is fairly large, the coefficient of variation would also be appropriate to look at. The coefficient of variation for the Upper West Side is 9.03% whereas the coefficient of variation for the Upper East Side is 9.06%. Therefore, relative to the mean, the variability in monthly rents on the Upper East Side is approximately the same as that on the Upper West Side.

II. A. Impossible
B. Possible
C. Possible
D. Possible
E. Possible

4 Data Presentation

A common problem faced by the researcher is how to properly summarize and present massive amounts of data that are collected in raw form so that the salient features of the data are more easily understood. Qualitative data may be tallied and presented as bar charts, as pie charts, as dot charts, or, where appropriate, as tables of cross-classification. On the other hand, quantitative data are often prepared and organized for tabular and chart presentation by forming ordered arrays and/or stem-and-leaf displays. (See Chapter 3.) However, to present the data in its most usual format, various tables (frequency distributions, percentage or relative frequency distributions, and cumulative distributions) and charts (histograms, polygons and ogives) are constructed. This chapter then focuses on methods of tabular and chart presentation as an aid to data analysis and interpretation.

MULTIPLE CHOICE

1. The width of each bar in a histogram corresponds to the

    (a) boundaries of the classes.
    (b) number of observations in the classes.
    (c) midpoint of the classes.
    (d) percentage of observations in the classes.

2. When constructing charts the following is plotted at class midpoints:

    (a) frequency histograms
    (b) percentage polygons
    (c) cumulative relative frequency ogives
    (d) dot charts

3. When comparing two or more sets of data of unequal sample sizes which are summarized into frequency distributions, it is most appropriate to examine the respective

   (a) frequency distributions.
   (b) frequency histograms.
   (c) cumulative frequency distributions.
   (d) relative frequency polygons.

4. When pictorially comparing two sets of quantitative data we should not use

   (a) percentage polygons.
   (b) side-by-side stem-and-leaf displays.
   (c) percentage ogives.
   (d) percentage pie charts.

5. Which of the following graphical presentations is inappropriate for qualitative data?

   (a) dot charts.
   (b) percentage pie charts
   (c) percentage ogives
   (d) percentage bar charts

6. When studying the simultaneous responses to two qualitative questions we should set up a

   (a) contingency table.
   (b) frequency distribution table.
   (c) cumulative percentage distribution table.
   (d) histogram.

7. In general, which of the following descriptive summary measures cannot be easily approximated from the percentage ogive?

   (a) range
   (b) median

   (c) variance)
   (d) mode

EXAMPLES

I. Raw data representing the lifetimes (in hours) of a random sample of 40 Brand A premium dry cell batteries and a random sample of 40 Brand B premium dry cell batteries have been collected.

Brand A				Brand B			
656	740	708	800	756	841	776	700
639	632	805	919	700	676	738	748
723	848	721	698	836	732	719	680
809	667	681	836	602	844	683	689
805	749	844	718	571	698	819	761
818	822	712	684	576	724	823	833
803	776	767	879	805	768	677	797
672	827	687	890	716	598	725	789
734	913	745	789	826	626	736	718
698	699	853	846	610	683	849	747

21

A. For each brand:

(1) place the raw data in an ordered array;
(2) place the raw data in a stem-and-leaf display (let the "leaves" be the units digit);
(3) establish class intervals and tally the data into the appropriate class groups to form the frequency distributions;
(4) form the relative frequency and percentage distributions;
(5) form the cumulative relative frequency distribution;
(6) plot the frequency histogram.

B. On one graph plot the relative frequency polygons for each brand.

C. On one graph plot the ogives (cumulative "less than" relative frequency polygons) for each brand.

D. Use the data for Brands A and B and form the cross-classification table for premium dry cell batteries lasting less than 800 hours versus those lasting at least 800 hours.

E. Write a brief summary comparing and contrasting the two brands.

SOLUTION

A. (1) Ordered Arrays of Brand A versus Brand B Premium Dry Cell Batteries

Brand A					Brand B			
632	699	767	827		571	683	732	797
639	708	776	836		576	689	736	805
656	712	789	844		598	698	738	819
667	718	800	846		602	700	747	823
672	721	803	848		610	700	748	826
681	723	805	853		626	716	756	833
684	734	805	879		676	718	761	836
687	740	809	890		677	719	768	841
698	745	818	913		680	724	776	844
698	749	822	919		683	725	789	849

(2) Stem-and-Leaf Display: Brand A & Brand B Premium Dry Cell Batteries

Brand A		Brand B	
63 & 64	9 2	57 & 58	1 6
65 & 66	6 7	59 & 60	2 8
67 & 68	2 1 7 4	61 & 62	0 6
69 & 70	8 9 8 8	63 & 64	
71 & 72	3 1 2 8	65 & 66	
73 & 74	4 0 9 5	67 & 68	6 3 3 7 0 9
75 & 76	7	69 & 70	0 8 0
77 & 78	6 9	71 & 72	6 4 9 5 8
79 & 80	9 5 3 5 0	73 & 74	2 8 6 8 7
81 & 82	8 2 7	75 & 76	6 8 1
83 & 84	8 4 6 6	77 & 78	6 9
85 & 86	3	79 & 80	5 7
87 & 88	9	81 & 82	6 9 3
89 & 90	0	83 & 84	6 1 4 9 3
91 & 92	3 9		

22

(3) Class Intervals and Frequency Distributions

Brand A: Width of Interval = $\dfrac{\text{Range}}{\text{No. of Class Groupings}}$

$$\frac{919 - 632}{5} = \frac{287}{5} = 57.4$$

For convenience and ease of reading, the selected interval (or width of each class grouping) for Brand A is rounded to 60.

Worksheet for Frequency Distribution

Lifetimes of Premium Dry Cell Batteries (in hours)	Frequency Tallies	
630 but less than 690	#### ///	8
690 but less than 750	#### #### //	12
750 but less than 810	#### ///	8
810 but less than 870	#### ///	8
870 but less than 930	////	4
Total		40

Brand B: For comparative purposes we will use, whenever possible, the same interval widths and class groupings as for Brand A.

Worksheet for Frequency Distribution

Lifetimes of Premium Dry Cell Batteries (in hours)	Frequency Tallies	
570 but less than 630	#### /	6
630 but less than 690	#### /	6
690 but less than 750	#### #### ///	13
750 but less than 810	#### //	7
810 but less than 870	#### ///	8
Total		40

Frequency Distributions of Premium Dry Cell Batteries

Lifetimes of Premium Dry Cell Batteries (in hours)	Frequency	
	Brand A	Brand B
570 but less than 630	-	6
630 but less than 690	8	6
690 but less than 750	12	13
750 but less than 810	8	7
810 but less than 870	8	8
870 but less than 930	4	-
Totals	40	40

(4) Relative frequency and percentage distributions.

RELATIVE FREQUENCY DISTRIBUTION AND PERCENTAGE DISTRIBUTION OF PREMIUM DRY CELL BATTERIES FOR BRAND A AND BRAND B

Lifetimes of Premium Dry Cell Batteries (in hours)	Brand A		Brand B	
	Relative Frequency	Percentage	Relative Frequency	Percentage
570 but less than 630	--	--	.15	15.0
630 but less than 690	.20	20.0	.15	15.0
690 but less than 750	.30	30.0	.325	32.5
750 but less than 810	.20	20.0	.175	17.5
810 but less than 870	.20	20.0	.20	20.0
870 but less than 930	.10	10.0	--	--
Totals	1.00	100.0	1.00	100.0

(5) Cumulative relative frequency distributions.

CUMULATIVE RELATIVE FREQUENCY DISTRIBUTION OF PREMIUM DRY CELL BATTERIES FOR BRAND A AND BRAND B

Lifetimes of Premium Dry Cell Batteries (in hours)	Brand A	Brand B
	< Value	< Value
570	---	.000
630	.000	.150
690	.200	.300
750	.500	.625
810	.700	.800
870	.900	1.000
930	1.000	1.000

(6) Frequency histograms.

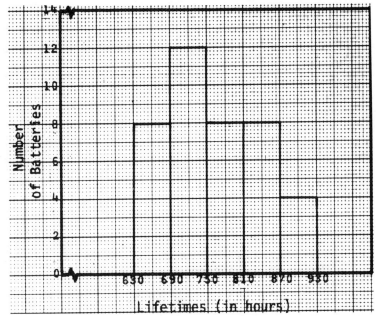

FREQUENCY HISTOGRAM OF PREMIUM DRY CELL BATTERIES FOR BRAND A
Source: Frequency Distribution for Brand A.

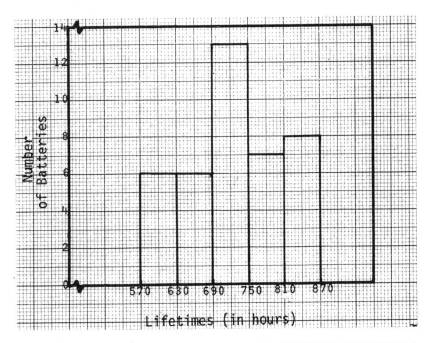

FREQUENCY HISTOGRAM OF PREMIUM DRY CELL BATTERIES FOR BRAND B
Source: Frequency Distribution for Brand B.

B.

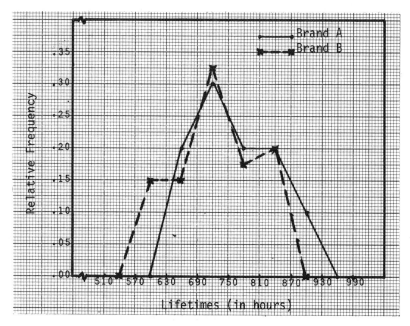

RELATIVE FREQUENCY POLYGONS OF PREMIUM DRY CELL
BATTERIES FOR BRAND A AND BRAND B

C.

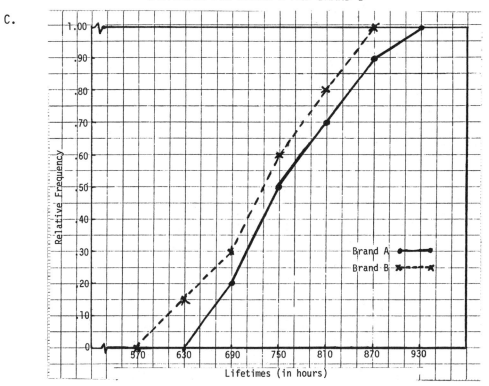

CUMULATIVE RELATIVE FREQUENCY POLYGONS OF PREMIUM
DRY CELL BATTERIES FOR BRAND A AND BRAND B

D. Cross-classification table for premium dry cell batteries lasting less than 800 hours versus those lasting at least 800 hours.

	Brand A	Brand B	Totals
Less than 800 hours	23	31	54
At least 800 hours	17	9	26
Totals	40	40	80

E.   We may conclude from a comparison of the distributions and polygons of the two brands that Brand A premium dry cell batteries are better than Brand B. The ranges in the lifetimes of Brand A and Brand B batteries are both 300 hours. However, the lifetimes of Brand A batteries (630 to 930) are longer than Brand B batteries (570 to 870). From the cumulative relative frequency distribution and ogives, there are no Brand A batteries that last less than 630 hours while 15% of the Brand B batteries last less than 630 hours. On the other hand, there are no Brand B batteries that last more than 870 hours while 10% of the Brand A batteries last more than 870 hours. Moreover, the middle value (called the median) is larger for Brand A batteries than Brand B batteries; that is, 50% of Brand A batteries last at least 750 hours whereas 50% of Brand B batteries last at least 727 hours. Finally, from the table of cross-classification we see that 17 out of the 40 Brand A batteries (42.5%) last at least 800 hours while only 9 out of the 40 Brand B batteries (22.5%) last that long.

(Grouped Data Approximations)

II. A hardware distributor reports the following distribution of sales from a sample of 100 sales receipts.

Dollar Value of Sales	Number of Sales (f)
$ 0 but less than 20	16
20 but less than 40	18
40 but less than 60	14
60 but less than 80	24
80 but less than 100	20
100 but less than 120	8
Total	100

A. Find the arithemtic mean.
B. Find the variance (definitional)
C. Find the standard deviation.

SOLUTION

A. Computation of the arithmetic mean.

Dollar Value of Sales	Class Marks m_j	No. of Sales f_j	$m_j f_j$
$ 0 but less than 20	10	16	160
20 but less than 40	30	18	540
40 but less than 60	50	14	700
60 but less than 80	70	24	1,680
80 but less than 100	90	20	1,800
100 but less than 120	110	8	880
Totals		100	$5,760

$$\bar{X} \approx \frac{\sum_{j=1}^{g} m_j f_j}{n} = \frac{\$5,760}{100} = \$57.60.$$

(Note: g = number of groups or classes in frequency distribution.)

B. Computation of variance using definitional method.

Definitional formula for variance: $s^2 \approx \dfrac{\sum_{j=1}^{g} (m_j - \bar{X})^2 f_j}{n - 1}$

28

Dollar Value of Sales	f_j	Class Marks m_j	$(m_j - \bar{X})$	$(m_j - \bar{X})^2$	$(m_j - \bar{X})^2 f_j$
$ 0 but less than 20	16	10	-47.60	2,265.76	36,252.16
20 but less than 40	18	30	-27.60	761.76	13,711.68
40 but less than 60	14	50	-7.60	57.76	808.64
60 but less than 80	24	70	12.40	153.76	3,690.24
80 but less than 100	20	90	32.40	1,049.76	20,995.20
100 but less than 120	8	110	52.40	2,745.76	21,966.08
Totals	100				97,424.00

$\bar{X} = \$57.60$

$$s^2 = \frac{\sum_{j=1}^{6} (m_j - \bar{X})^2 f_j}{100 - 1} = \frac{97,424.00}{99} = 984.0808.$$

C. Standard deviation $= \sqrt{s^2} = \sqrt{984.0808} = \$31.37$.

III. The following summary table shows the dollar sales (in millions of dollars) of product X according to census region in the past year:

Census Region	Sales
North East	$240
North Central	120
South	160
West	280
Total	$800

A. Convert the data to percentages.

B. Construct a percentage dot chart.

A. Conversion of data to percentages.

Census Region	Percentages
North East	30.0
North Central	15.0
South	20.0
West	35.0
Total	100.0

B.

Percentage dot chart of dollar sales of product X by Census Regions.

REVIEW PROBLEMS

I. Bottoms-up and Bottoms-down are competitors for the diet soft drink market. Based on separate random samples of n=25 test tubes (each containing one fluid ounce) raw data are collected on the saccharin content (in
milligrams per fluid ounce) of the two competing diet soft drinks.

Bottoms-up (n=25)			Bottoms-down (n=25)		
6.15	6.23	6.14	6.38	6.27	6.24
5.95	6.13	6.19	6.05	6.10	6.12
6.17	6.16	6.06	6.17	6.06	6.25
5.92	6.15	6.09	6.11	6.19	6.35
6.12	5.97	5.98	6.31	6.23	6.33
6.20	5.89	6.03	6.02	6.26	6.21
6.18	6.14	6.15	6.26	6.29	6.16
5.99	6.00	6.13	6.32	6.15	6.26
6.11			6.37		

A. For Bottoms-up and Bottoms-down:

(1) Place the raw data in an ordered array.

30

(2) Place the raw data in a stem-and-leaf display. (Hint: Use the hundreths digit as the leaves.)

(3) Using class groupings of 5.84 but less than 5.92; 5.92 but less than 6.00; 6.00 but less than 6.08, etc., form the frequency and percentage distributions.

(4) Form the cumulative percentage distributions.

(5) Plot the frequency histogram.

B. On one graph plot the percentage polygons for each group.

C. On one graph plot the ogives for each group.

II. Consider a group of business students that consist of 32 accounting majors, 24 marketing majors, 8 management majors, 12 computer methodology/statistics majors and 4 economics/finance majors.

   A. Form a summary table according to student major by frequencies and percentages.

   B. Construct a percentage dot chart.

III. A survey was conducted to investigate the possible relationships between political attitudes and political party affiliation for 300 Manhattan residents. The sample contained 100 democrats, 100 republicans, and 100 independents. They shared their views on the nuclear arms freeze (for/against), capital punishment (for/against), and abortion (for/against). 85 democrats were in favor of the nuclear arms freeze, as were 2 republicans and 55 independents. 14 democrats were against capital punishment, as were 65 republicans and 46 independents. Half of the democrats, republicans, and independents surveyed favored abortion.

   Form a supertable of these responses.

IV. A random sample of 100 managers was selected from among various departments in a large Wall Street firm and the annual absenteeism of these managers was obtained. Absenteeism ranged from 1 day to 74 days. Set up the class boundaries for a frequency distribution.

   A. If 5 class intervals are desired.
   B. If 7 class intervals are desired.
   C. If 10 class intervals are desired.
   D. What are the 10 class midpoints for (C)?

   (Remember: Avoid overlapping intervals)

V. The figure below contains the cumulative relative frequency polygons (ogives) of math ability scores for two random samples (A and B) of 100 students each drawn from two New York City Community Colleges. Based on these data, answer each of the following questions.

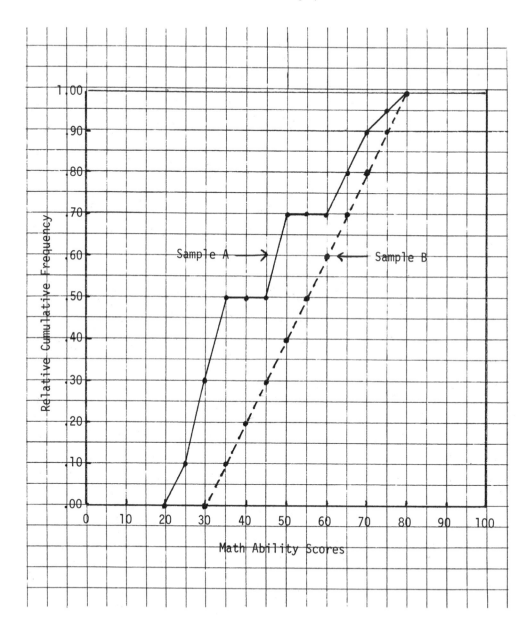

A. How many students in sample A have math ability scores of 70 or more?
B. What is the percentage of students in sample A with math ability scores of less than 65?
C. Which sample has a larger range of math ability scores?
D. How many students in sample A have math ability scores of at least 50 but less than 60?
E. Does sample A or sample B have more students with math ability scores of 65 or above?
F. What percentage of sample A students have math ability scores less than 50?
G. What percentage of sample A students have math ability scores of 50 or more?
H. Which sample has more students with math ability scores below 80?

VI. Sketch a polygon such that the following is true:

A. The mean, median, and mode are identical.

B. The mean is greater than the median.

C. The median is greater than the mean.

VII. Based on the frequency distributions of the rate of interest on home mortgages in metro areas A and B, the following graphs have been drawn:

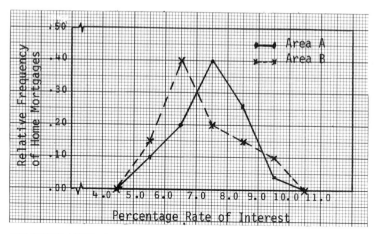

RELATIVE FREQUENCY POLYGONS OF THE PERCENTAGE RATE OF
INTEREST ON HOME MORTGAGES IN METRO AREAS A AND B

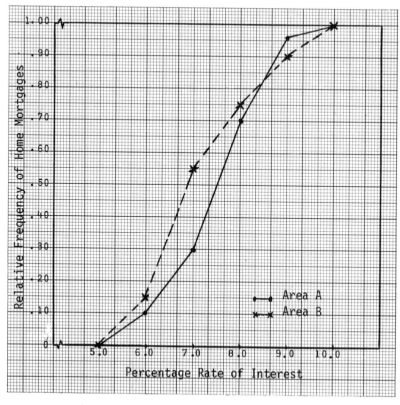

CUMULATIVE ("LESS THAN") RELATIVE FREQUENCY POLYGONS OF THE
PERCENTAGE RATE OF INTEREST ON HOME MORTGAGES IN METRO AREAS A AND B

Based upon the graphs, answer each of the following questions.

(1) The median percentage rate of interest is

    (a) larger for Metro Area A.
    (b) larger for Metro Area B.
    (c) the same for both metro areas.

(2) The metro area that has a <u>higher</u> proportion of home mortgages at an interest rate between 8.00 and under 9.00 percent is

    (a) Metro Area A.
    (b) Metro Area B.
    (c) undeterminable.

(3) In Metro Area B the proportion of home mortgages with interest rates below 8 percent is

    (a) .70.
    (b) .75.
    (c) .25.

(4) In Metro Area A the percentage of home mortgages with interest rates of 7 percent or more is

    (a) 45%
    (b) 70%
    (c) 30%

(5) The interquartile range is

    (a) smaller for Metro Area A.
    (b) smaller for Metro Area B.
    (c) about the same for both metro areas.

(6) The range of percentage rate of interest is

    (a) narrower for Metro Area A.
    (b) narrower for Metro Area B.
    (c) the same for both metro areas.

(7) In Metro Area A, the <u>number</u> of home mortgages with interest rates below 6 percent are

    (a) 15
    (b) 5
    (c) 10

(8) The mode is

    (a) larger for Metro Area A.
    (b) larger for Metro Area B.
    (c) impossible to approximate from the graphs.

(9) The metro area that has the <u>lower</u> proportion of home mortgages with interest rates of less than 8 percent is

    (a) Metro Area A.
    (b) Metro Area B.
    (c) impossible to approximate from the graphs.

(10) The metro area that has the <u>lower</u> proportion of home mortgages with interest rates of at least 7 percent is

    (a) Metro Area A.
    (b) Metro Area B.
    (c) impossible to approximate from the graphs.

SOLUTIONS TO REVIEW PROBLEMS

I. A. (1) Ordered arrays

Bottoms-up			Bottoms-down		
5.89	6.09	6.15	6.02	6.19	6.27
5.92	6.11	6.15	6.05	6.21	6.29
5.95	6.12	6.16	6.06	6.23	6.31
5.97	6.13	6.17	6.10	6.24	6.32
5.98	6.13	6.18	6.11	6.25	6.33
5.99	6.14	6.19	6.12	6.26	6.35
6.00	6.14	6.20	6.15	6.26	6.37
6.03	6.15	6.23	6.16	6.26	6.38
6.06			6.17		

(2) Stem-and-Leaf Display of Saccharin Content (in milligrams per fluid ounce) in Bottoms-up and Bottoms-down

Bottoms-up

5.8	9
5.9	5 2 9 7 8
6.0	0 6 9 3
6.1	5 7 2 8 1 3 6 5 4 4 9 5 3
6.2	0 3

Bottoms-down

6.0	5 2 6
6.1	7 1 0 9 5 2 6
6.2	6 7 3 6 9 4 5 1 6
6.3	8 1 2 7 5 3

38

(3) Frequency and Percentage Distributions of Saccharin Content
(per fluid ounce) in Bottoms-up and Bottoms-down

Saccharin Content (in milligrams)	Bottoms-up		Bottoms-down	
	Frequency	Percentage	Frequency	Percentage
5.84 but less than 5.92	1	4.0	-	--
5.92 but less than 6.00	5	20.0	-	--
6.00 but less than 6.08	3	12.0	3	12.0
6.08 but less than 6.16	10	40.0	4	16.0
6.16 but less than 6.24	6	24.0	5	20.0
6.24 but less than 6.32	-	--	8	32.0
6.32 but less than 6.40	-	--	5	20.0
Totals	25	100.0	25	100.0

(4) Cumulative Percentage Distributions of Saccharin Content (per
fluid ounce) in Bottoms-up and Bottoms-down

Saccharin Content (in milligrams)	Bottoms-up	Bottoms-down
	< Value	< Value
5.84	0.0	--
5.92	4.0	--
6.00	24.0	0.0
6.08	36.0	12.0
6.16	76.0	28.0
6.24	100.0	48.0
6.32	100.0	80.0
6.40	100.0	100.0

(5)

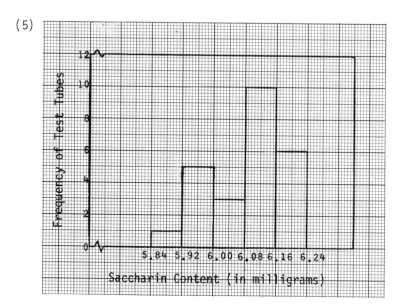

FREQUENCY HISTOGRAM OF SACCHARIN CONTENT (PER
FLUID OUNCE) IN BOTTOMS-UP DIET SOFT DRINK

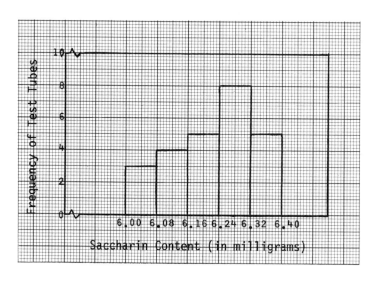

FREQUENCY HISTOGRAM OF SACCHARIN CONTENT (PER
FLUID OUNCE) IN BOTTOMS-DOWN DIET SOFT DRINK

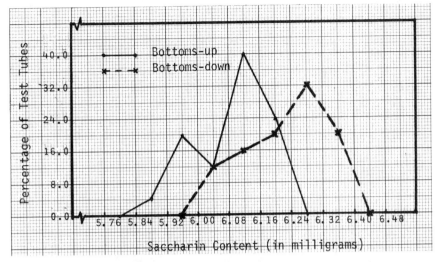

PERCENTAGE POLYGONS OF SACCHARIN CONTENT (PER FLUID OUNCE)
IN BOTTOMS-UP AND BOTTOMS-DOWN DIET SOFT DRINKS

C.

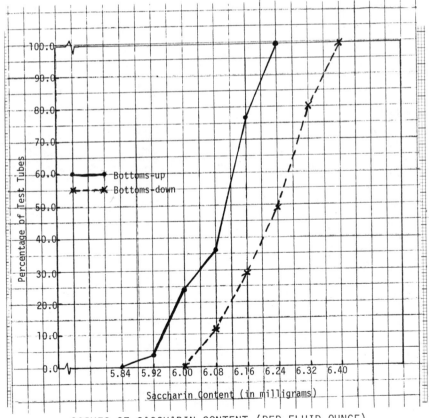

OGIVES OF SACCHARIN CONTENT (PER FLUID OUNCE)
IN BOTTOMS-UP AND BOTTOMS-DOWN DIET SOFT DRINKS

II. A. Frequency and Percentage Table According to Business Students Major

Major	Frequency	Percentage
Accounting	32	40.0
Marketing	24	30.0
Management	8	10.0
Computer Methodology/ Statistics	12	15.0
Economics/Finance	4	5.0
Totals	80	100.0

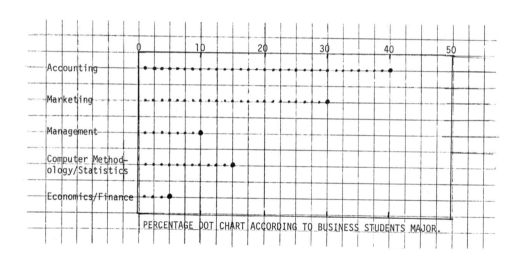

PERCENTAGE DOT CHART ACCORDING TO BUSINESS STUDENTS MAJOR.

III. A Supertable for Studying Possible Relationships Between Political
        Attitudes and Political Party Affiliation for 300
                    Manhattan Residents*

Variables and Category Percentages	Political Party Affiliation		
	Democrats	Republicans	Independents
Nuclear Arms Freeze:			
For (47%)	59.9%	1.4%	38.7%
Against (53%)	9.5%	62.0%	28.5%
Capital Punishment:			
For (58%)	49.1%	20.0%	30.9%
Against (42%)	11.2%	52.0%	36.8%
Abortion:			
For (50%)	33.3%	33.3%	33.3%
Against (50%)	33.3%	33.3%	33.3%

*Percentages have been rounded.

IV. A. Width of interval = $\dfrac{\text{Range}}{\text{Number of desired class groupings}}$

$$= \frac{74-1}{5} = \frac{73}{5} = 14.6$$

For convenience and ease of reading, the width of each class
interval is rounded up to 15.

Absenteeism

    0 days but less than 15 days
   15 days but less than 30 days
   30 days but less than 45 days
   45 days but less than 60 days
   60 days but less than 75 days

B. We follow the same procedure for determing the width of the interval
as in (A). However, the number of desired class groupings is 7.

Hence, $\dfrac{74-1}{7} = \dfrac{73}{7} = 10.4$

Again, for convenience, the width of each class interval is
rounded (up to 11).

Absenteeism

 0 days but less than 11 days
11 days but less than 22 days
22 days but less than 33 days
33 days but less than 44 days
44 days but less than 55 days
55 days but less than 66 days
66 days but less than 77 days

C. Same procedure to determine interval width as used in (A) and (B).
We change the desired class groupings now to 10.

Hence, $\dfrac{74-1}{10} = \dfrac{73}{10} = 7.3$

As above, we round the width of each class interval (to 8).

Absenteeism

 0 days but less than 8 days
 8 days but less than 16 days
16 days but less than 24 days
24 days but less than 32 days
32 days but less than 40 days
40 days but less than 48 days
48 days but less than 56 days
56 days but less than 64 days
64 days but less than 72 days
72 days but less than 80 days

D. Class Midpoints for (C):

 4
12
20
28
36
44
52
60
68
76

V. A. 10 students
   B. 80%
   C. Sample A
   D. None
   E. Sample B
   F. 70%
   G. 30%
   H. Neither

44

VI.

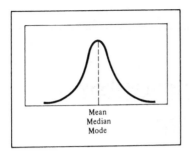

A.

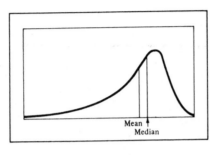

B.

C.

VII.   (1) a   (3) b   (5) a   (7) b   (9) a
        (2) a   (4) b   (6) c   (8) a   (10) b

45

5 Using the Computer for Descriptive Statistical Analysis

To this point we have studied how collected data are prepared, summarized, characterized, and presented. This chapter discusses how appropriate computer software can help us in statistically analyzing our data. To interact properly with the computer, the user must be familiar with the software packages currently on the market, as well as know how to select appropriate statistical procedures for the tasks at hand. For further discussion and a more detailed outline of how this may be accomplished, please refer to chapter 5 in your textbook.

6 Basic Probability

In this chapter various rules of probability are examined. The concept of an event and a sample space are developed to provide a means of evaluating simple and joint probabilities using either a contingency table or Venn diagram. These principles are extended to conditional probability, the multiplication rule, and the addition rule. Conditional probability is illustrated by using Bayes' theorem (for revising probabilities). Various counting rules, including permutations and combinations, are then discussed for situations in which there are a larger number of favorable outcomes.

MULTIPLE CHOICE

1. The event "picking a black king" from a deck of cards is an example of a

    (a) simple event.   (c) sample space.
    (b) joint event.   (d) complement of an event.

2. In a Venn diagram, the term A ∩ B represents

    (a) the intersection of circles A and B.
    (b) the area included in circle A or circle B.
    (c) the area outside the two circles.
    (d) None of the above.

3. If two events are mutually exclusive, the probability of their intersection is equal to

    (a) 0.   (c) .50.
    (b) 1.0.   (d) Cannot be determined.

4. If the outcome of event A is not affected by event B, then events A and B are said to be

   (a) mutually exclusive.   (c) collectively exhaustive.
   (b) statistically independent.   (d) None of the above.

5. The number of different ways that eight people could be seated around the table would be computed from

   (a) 8^8 (c) $8!$
   (b) $8 \cdot 8$ (d) $8!/4!4!$

6. The number of ways that 5 workers could be selected from 100 workers for an early lunch hour would be computed from

   (a) 5^{100} (c) $100!/95!$
   (b) $5 \cdot 100$ (d) $100!/5!95!$

EXAMPLES

I. A survey is conducted by the Federal Government to determine if their employees would like to switch over to a more flexible weekly work schedule (i.e., 8 a.m. to 4 p.m. or 10 a.m. to 6 p.m. or 4 ten-hour days, etc.) or to stay on a standard (9 a.m. to 5 p.m.) work schedule. Questionnaires were mailed out to 1,000 randomly selected employees in four geographic regions--NorthEast, Central, West and South. The following table shows the results of the survey:

| Preference | Geographic Regions | | | | |
	NE (NorthEast)	C (Central)	W (West)	S (South)	Totals
F (More Flexible Work Schedule)	192	96	224	128	640
F' (Standard)	108	54	126	72	360
Totals	300	150	350	200	1,000

If a Federal employee is randomly selected, what is the probability that

   (a) he wants to switch to a more flexible work schedule?
   (b) he lives in the South?
   (c) he wants to switch to a more flexible work schedule and he lives in the West?
   (d) he wants to maintain the standard work schedule or he lives in the NorthEast?
   (e) If the employee selected wants to switch to a more flexible work schedule, what is the probability he lives in the Central region?
   (f) Is the opinion of the employee statistically independent of the geographic region he lives in?

48

SOLUTION

(a) $P(F) = \dfrac{640}{1,000} = .64.$

(b) $P(S) = \dfrac{200}{1,000} = .20.$

(c) By formula the joint probability $P(F \cap W) = P(F|W)P(W)$

$$= \left(\dfrac{224}{350}\right)\left(\dfrac{350}{1,000}\right) = \dfrac{224}{1,000} = .224.$$

We could have also found $P(F \cap W)$ by directly finding the number of people who want to switch and live in the West from the table and dividing by the total number of employees. (i.e., $P(F \cap W) = 224/1,000 = .224$)

(d) $P(F' \cup NE) = P(F') + P(NE) - P(F' \cap NE)$

$$= \dfrac{360}{1,000} + \dfrac{300}{1,000} - \dfrac{108}{1,000} = \dfrac{552}{1,000} = .552.$$

(e) By formula the conditional probability $P(C|F) = \dfrac{P(C \cap F)}{P(F)}$

$$= \dfrac{96/1,000}{640/1,000} = \dfrac{96}{640} = .15.$$

We could have also found $P(C|F)$ by first looking at those who want to switch to a more flexible schedule (640) and then finding the number of these who live in the Central region (96). Finally, we would find the proportion of these people who want to switch who live in the Central region (i.e., $P(C|F) = 96/640 = .15$).

(f) Since the conditional probability, $P(C|F) = .15$, is equal to the marginal probability, $P(C) = 150/1,000 = .15$, the opinion of the employee is statistically independent of geographic region.

II. In a meat packaging plant, machines X and Y account for 60% and 40% of the plant's output, respectively. It is known that 1% of the packages from machine X and 2% of the packages from machine Y are improperly sealed.

(a) If a package is selected at random, what is the probability that it will be improperly sealed?
(b) If the package selected at random is improperly sealed, what is the probability that it came from machine X?

SOLUTION

(a) Probability that package selected is improperly sealed (i.e., $P(I)$).

Machine (M_i)	Probability $P(M_i)$	Conditional Probability $P(I\|M_i)$	Joint Probability $P(I\|M_i)\,P(M_i)$
X	.60	.01	.01(.60) = .006
Y	.40	.02	.02(.40) = .008
	1.00		$P(I)$ = .014

$$P(I) = \text{sum of joint probabilities} = \sum_{i=1}^{2} P(I \cap M_i) = \sum_{i=1}^{2} P(I\|M_i)\,P(M_i)$$

$$= P(I\|X)P(X) + P(I\|Y)P(Y) = .006 + .008 = .014.$$

(b) Using Bayes' theorem we can find the probability that an improperly sealed package came from machine X (i.e., $P(X\|I)$).

$$P(X\|I) = \frac{P(I \cap X)}{P(I)} = \frac{P(I \cap X)}{P(I \cap X) + P(I \cap Y)}$$

$$= \frac{P(I\|X)P(X)}{P(I\|X)P(X) + P(I\|Y)P(Y)} = \frac{.006}{.006 + .008} = \frac{.006}{.014} = .429.$$

REVIEW PROBLEMS

I. In a city of 5,000 adults, 2,000 live in private homes while the remainder live in apartment buildings. Of those living in private homes, 240 are upper income, 1,200 are middle income and 560 are lower income. Of those living in apartment buildings, 900 are upper income, 600 are middle income and 1,500 are lower income.

   A. Set up a cross-classification table for type of dwelling and income status, to find the probability that a person chosen at random

   (1) is middle income
   (2) lives in an apartment building
   (3) lives in a private home and is upper income
   (4) lives in an apartment building or is lower income
   (5) is middle income, if it is known that he lives in an apartment building.

B. Is type of dwelling statistically independent of income?

II. Suppose that 40% of all New Yorkers like beer, 50% like wine and 20% like beer and wine. If a resident is chosen at random, find the probability that he

    (a) dislikes wine
    (b) likes beer or wine
    (c) dislikes beer but likes wine
    (d) If the resident selected likes wine, what is the probability that he dislikes beer?
    (e) Are the two tastes "liking beer" and "liking wine" statistically independent?

    (Hint: Set up a cross-classification (2 X 2) table for beer drinkers and wine drinkers.)

III. An electronics company has an engineering position open. The probability that an applicant is capable is .70. Each applicant is given a written and oral exam. A capable applicant passes with probability .90, while an incapable applicant passes with probability .40.

    (a) Find the probability that an applicant passes the test.

(b) Given that the applicant passes the test, what is the probability that he is capable?

SOLUTIONS TO REVIEW PROBLEMS

I.   A.

| | | Income Status | | | |
	Type of Dwelling	L (Lower)	M (Middle)	U (Upper)	Totals
A	(Apartment Building)	1,500	600	900	3,000
P	(Private Homes)	560	1,200	240	2,000
	Totals	2,060	1,800	1,140	5,000

(1) $P(M) = \dfrac{1,800}{5,000} = .36$.

(2) $P(A) = \dfrac{3,000}{5,000} = .60$.

(3) $P(P \cap U) = \dfrac{240}{5,000} = .048$.

(4) $P(A \cup L) = \dfrac{3,000}{5,000} + \dfrac{2,060}{5,000} - \dfrac{1,500}{5,000} = \dfrac{3,560}{5,000} = .712$.

(5) $P(M|A) = \dfrac{600}{3,000} = .20$.

B. Since $P(M|A) = .20$ does not equal $P(M) = .36$, type of dwelling is not statistically independent of income status.

II.

	B (Likes Beer)	B' (Dislikes Beer)	Totals
W (Likes Wine)	.20	.30	.50
W' (Dislikes Wine)	.20	.30	.50
Totals	.40	.60	1.00

(a) $P(W') = .50$.

(b) $P(B \cup W) = .40 + .50 - .20 = .70$.

(c) $P(B' \cap W) = .30$.

(d) $P(B'|W) = \frac{.30}{.50} = .60$.

(e) Since $P(B'|W) = .60$ does equal $P(B') = .60$, the two tastes, "liking beer" and "liking wine" are statistically independent.

III. Let C be capable applicant, C' be incapable applicant, P be passes test, and P' does not pass test.

Given: $P(C) = .70$, $P(P|C) = .90$, and $P(P|C') = .40$.

(a)

Capability C_i	$P(C_i)$	Conditional Probability $P(P|C_i)$	Joint Probability $P(P|C_i) \, P(C_i)$
C	.70	.90	.63
C'	.30	.40	.12
	1.00		$P(P) = .75$

P(passes test) is .75.

(b)

$$P(C|P) = \frac{P(C \cap P)}{P(P)} = \frac{P(P|C) \, P(C)}{P(P|C)P(C) + P(P|C')P(C')} = \frac{.63}{.63 + .12} = .84.$$

Basic Probability Distributions

In the previous chapter we established various rules of probability and examined some counting techniques. In this chapter we utilize this information to explore various probability models which represent certain phenomena of interest. In particular, the following discrete probability distributions are considered: the uniform distribution, the binomial distribution, the hypergeometric distribution and the Poisson distribution. In addition, for continuous probability models the normal distribution is described not only for its representation of numerous continuous phenomena, but also for its use in approximating discrete probability distributions in an effort to save computational drudgery. Such concepts as discrete versus continuous probability distributions, mathematical expectation, finite population correction factor, and the correction for continuity adjustment are discussed.

MULTIPLE CHOICE

1. In a probability distribution, the probabilities associated with the outcomes must

   (a) be constant.   (c) be decreasing.
   (b) be increasing.   (d) sum up to one.

2. The connotation "expected monetary value" or "expected gain" from playing Roulette at a casino means

   (a) the amount you expect to "gain" on a single play.
   (b) the amount you expect to "gain" in the long run over many plays.
   (c) the amount you need to "break even" over many plays.
   (d) the amount you should expect to gain if you are lucky.

3. If n=10 and p=.4

   (a) the variance of the binomial distribution is 4.0.
   (b) the variance of the binomial distribution is 2.4.
   (c) the standard deviation of the binomial distribution is 2.4.
   (d) the standard deviation of the binomial distribution is 4.0.

4. Theoretically, in a Poisson distribution

   (a) the mean equals the variance.
   (b) the variance equals the median.
   (c) the standard deviation equals the variance.
   (d) the standard deviation equals the mean.

5. The finite population correction factor is used when computing the standard deviation from the

   (a) uniform distribution.   (c) hypergeometric distribution.
   (b) binomial distribution.   (d) Poisson distribution.

6. The binomial distribution will be symmetrical when

   (a) n is small.   (c) np is .5.
   (b) p is .5.   (d) p is large.

7. Which of the following about the normal distribution is not true?

   (a) Theoretically, the mean, median and mode are the same.
   (b) About 2/3 of the observations fall within $\pm$ 1 standard deviation from the mean.
   (c) It is a discrete probability distribution.
   (d) Its parameters are the mean, μ, and standard deviation, σ.

EXAMPLES

I. To attract more customers, Burger Sting is holding a contest with the following prize list--one automobile, 1,200 hamburgers, 2,000 orders of french fries, 2,000 colas and 4,799 joke cards. The automobile is worth $2,500, each hamburger is worth 50¢, an order of french fries is worth 35¢ and each cola is worth 30¢. A joke card is worth nothing but a good laugh. To distribute these prizes, 10,000 tickets have been printed, with one prize on each ticket. Suppose a customer is given a randomly chosen ticket.

    (a) Set up a probability distribution of the prizes a customer can win.
    (b) Compute the expected (monetary) value of the ticket.
    (c) Compute the variance and standard deviation.

SOLUTION

    (a) Probability distribution of prizes:

Prizes	Value of Prizes (X_i)	Number	Probability $(P(X_i))$
Joke Card	$ .00	4,799	.4799
Cola	.30	2,000	.2000
French Fries	.35	2,000	.2000
Hamburger	.50	1,200	.1200
Automobile	2,500.00	1	.0001
		10,000	1.0000

(b) and (c) Computations for expected value, variance and standard deviation:

Value (X_i)	$P(X_i)$	$X_i P(X_i)$	$(X_i - \mu_x)$	$(X_i - \mu_x)^2$	$(X_i - \mu_x)^2 P(X_i)$
$ .00	.4799	$ .00	-.44	.1936	.0929
.30	.2000	.06	-.14	.0196	.0039
.35	.2000	.07	-.09	.0081	.0016
.50	.1200	.06	.06	.0036	.0004
2,500.00	.0001	.25	2,499.56	6,247,800.1936	624.7800
	1.0000	$ .44			624.8788

Expected Value: $\mu_x = E(X) = \sum_{i=1}^{N} X_i P(X_i) = \underline{\$.44}.$

Variance: $\sigma_X^2 = Var(X) = \sum_{i=1}^{N} (X_i \quad)^2 P(X_i) = \underline{624.8788}.$

Standard Deviation: $\sigma_X = \sqrt{Var(X)} = \sqrt{624.8788} = \underline{\$24.998}.$

II. The Adamson Life Insurance Company has determined that .0001 of the population incurs a rare disease each year. Assuming that the company has insured 10,000 people randomly selected from the population, what is the probability that

(a) none of the policyholders will incur a rare disease?
(b) at least two of the policyholders will incur a rare disease?
(c) no more than two of the policyholders will incur a rare disease?

SOLUTION

This is an example using the Poisson as an approximation to the binomial distribution. The results may be obtained directly from Table E.6, or can be computed as follows:

$$P(X=x|n,p) = \frac{e^{-np} (np)^x}{x!}$$

where

n = the sample size = 10,000
p = the true probability of incurring a rare disease = .0001
e = 2.71828 (the base of the natural logarithmic system)

and

x = the number of people who incur the rare disease in the sample.

(a)
$$P(X=0|\lambda=np=1.0) \approx \frac{e^{-1.0}(1.0)^0}{0!} = \frac{e^{-1.0}(1)}{1} = \frac{1}{e} = \underline{.3679}.$$

(b)
$$P(X\geq2|\lambda=np=1.0) \approx 1-(P(X=0)+P(X=1)) = 1 - (.3679 + \frac{e^{-1.0}(1.0)^1}{1!})$$

$$= 1 - (.3679 + .3679) = 1 - .7358 = \underline{.2642}.$$

(c)
$$P(X\leq2|\lambda=np=1.0) \approx P(X=0)+P(X=1)+P(X=2) = .3679 + .3679 + \frac{e^{-1.0}(1.0)^2}{2!}$$

$$= .3679 + .3679 + .1839 = \underline{.9197}.$$

III. A package of 5 light bulbs contains one "marginal" bulb. If a person selects two bulbs at random without replacement, find the probability that

(a) both are good.
(b) one is good and the other is "marginal."
(c) What would your answers to part (a) and (b) have been had the sample been drawn with replacement?

SOLUTION

Part (a) and (b) are examples using the hypergeometric distribution:

$$P(X=x|n,N,A) = \frac{\binom{A}{X}\binom{N-A}{n-X}}{\binom{N}{n}}$$

where
- n = the sample size = 2
- N = the population size = 5
- A = the number of good bulbs in population = 4
- X = the number of good bulbs in sample
- $N-A$ = the number of "marginal" bulbs in population = 1.

(a)
$$P(X=2|n=2,N=5,A=4) = \frac{\binom{4}{2}\binom{1}{0}}{\binom{5}{2}} = \frac{\frac{4!}{2!2!}(1)}{\frac{5!}{2!3!}} = \frac{6}{10} = \underline{.6}.$$

(b)
$$P(X=1|n=2,N=5,A=4) = \frac{\binom{4}{1}\binom{1}{1}}{\binom{5}{2}} = \frac{\frac{4!}{1!3!}(1)}{\frac{5!}{2!3!}} = \frac{4}{10} = \underline{.4}.$$

(c)

When the bulb is replaced before the next selection, the proportion of good bulbs becomes constant for each selection. Therefore, we have a binomial distribution problem (see Table E.7).

$$(1)\ P(X=2|n=2,p=.8) = \frac{2!}{2!0!}(.8)^2(.2)^0 = \underline{.64}.$$

$$(2)\ P(X=1|n=2,p=.8) = \frac{2!}{1!1!}(.8)^1(.2)^1 = \underline{.32}.$$

Moreover, it is also possible to draw the "marginal" bulb twice:

$$P(X=0|n=2,p=.8) = \frac{2!}{0!2!}(.8)^0(.2)^2 = \underline{.04}.$$

IV. In a game called Taxation and Evasion, a player rolls a pair of dice. If, on any turn, the sum is 7, 11 or 12 the player gets audited. Otherwise, she evades taxes.

   A. If a player takes 5 turns at rolling the dice, find the probability that

   (1) she does not get audited.
   (2) she gets audited once.
   (3) she gets audited no more than two times.

   B. What is the expected number of times she will be audited?

   C. If a player takes 192 turns at rolling the dice, what is the approximate probability that

   (1) she gets audited between 40 and 62 times?
   (2) she gets audited at most 55 times?

SOLUTION

   A. This is an example using the binomial probability distribution:

   $$P(X=x|n,p) = \frac{n!}{x!(n-x)!}\ p^x(1-p)^{n-x}$$

   where

   n = the number of times she rolls a pair of dice = 5
   x = the number of times she gets audited
   p = the proportion of times she gets audited = proportion
       of times she rolls a 7, 11 or 12 (which is 6/36 + 2/36
       + 1/36 = 9/36 = .25)
   1-p = the proportion of times she evades taxes = 1-.25 = .75

   $$(1)\ P(x=0) = \frac{5!}{0!5!}(.25)^0(.75)^5 = (1)(1)(.2373) = \underline{.2373}.$$

   $$(2)\ P(x=1) = \frac{5!}{1!4!}(.25)^1(.75)^4 = \frac{5 \times 4!}{1 \times 4!}(.25)(.31640625)$$

   $$= 5(.25)(.31640625) = \underline{.3955}.$$

(3) $P(X \leq 2) = P(x=0)+P(x=1)+P(x=2) = .2373 + .3955 + \frac{5!}{2!3!}(.25)^2(.75)^3$

$$= .6328 + 10(.0625)(.421875) = .6328 + .2637 = \underline{.8965}.$$

B. $\mu_X = E(X) = np = 5(.25) = 1.25.$ On the average, she may expect to be audited <u>1.25 times</u>.

C. As n gets large such that $np \geq 5$ and $n(1-p) \geq 5$, the normal distribution can be used as an approximation to the binomial distribution (see Table E.2). In this example,

$$\mu_X = np = 192(.25) = 48 \text{ and}$$

$$\sigma_X = \sqrt{np(1-p)} = \sqrt{192(.25)(.75)} = \sqrt{36} = 6$$

Without "correction for continuity" as indicated in Section 7.11:

$$Z \simeq \frac{X - \mu_X}{\sigma_X}$$

(1) $P(40 \leq X \leq 62) = ?$

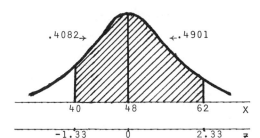

.4082→   ←.4901

$$Z \simeq \frac{X - \mu_X}{\sigma_X} = \frac{X - np}{\sqrt{np(1-p)}} = \frac{40 - 48}{6} = -1.33$$

$$Z \simeq \frac{62 - 48}{6} = \frac{14}{6} = 2.33$$

$$P(40 \leq X \leq 62) \simeq .4082 + .4901 = \underline{.8983}.$$

(2) $P(X \leq 55) = ?$

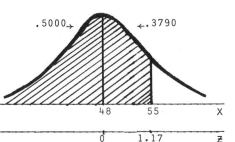

.5000→   ←.3790

$$Z \simeq \frac{55 - 48}{6} = \frac{7}{6} = 1.17$$

$$P(X \leq 55) \simeq .5000 + .3790 = \underline{.8790}.$$

59

With "correction for continuity" as indicated in Section 7.12:

$$Z \approx \frac{(X - \mu_X) \pm .5}{\sigma_X}$$

(1) $P(40 \leq X \leq 62) = ?$

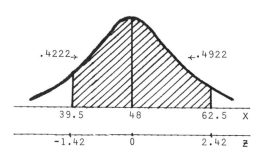

$$Z \approx \frac{40 - 48 - .5}{6} = \frac{-8.5}{6} = -1.42$$

$$Z \approx \frac{62 - 48 + .5}{6} = \frac{14.5}{6} = 2.42$$

$$P(39.5 \leq X \leq 62.5) = .4222 + .4922$$

$$= .9144.$$

(2) $P(X \leq 55) = ?$

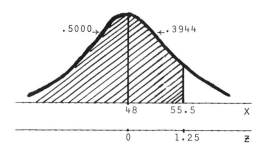

$$Z \approx \frac{55 - 48 + .5}{6} = \frac{7.5}{6} = 1.25$$

$$P(X \leq 55) \approx P(X \leq 55.5)$$

$$= .5000 + .3944 = .8944.$$

In this particular example the correction for continuity increases accuracy.

V. In a particular industry the average wage is $4.90 per hour and the standard deviation is $.40. If the wages are assumed to be normally distributed,

(a) what percentage of the workers receive wages between $3.90 and $4.90?
(b) what percentage of the workers receive wages between $3.80 and $5.40?
(c) what percentage of the workers receive wages between $5.20 and $6.10?
(d) what percentage of the workers receive wages less than $4.00?
(e) what percentage of the workers receive wages more than $5.95?
(f) what percentage of the workers receive wages less than $4.00 or more than $5.95?
(g) what must the wage be if only 10 percent of all workers in this particular industry earn more?
(h) what must the wage be if only 25 percent of all workers in this particular industry earn less?

SOLUTION

(a) $P(3.90 \leq X \leq 4.90) = ?$

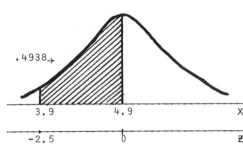

$Z = \dfrac{X - \mu_X}{\sigma_X} = \dfrac{3.90 - 4.90}{.40} = \dfrac{-1}{.40} = -2.50$

$P(3.90 \leq X \leq 4.90) = .4938$ or 49.38%

(b) $P(3.80 \leq X \leq 5.40) = ?$

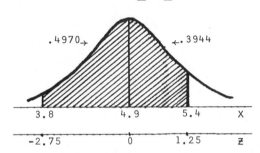

$Z = \dfrac{3.80 - 4.90}{.40} = \dfrac{-1.1}{.40} = -2.75$

$Z = \dfrac{5.40 - 4.90}{.40} = \dfrac{.50}{.40} = 1.25$

$P(3.80 \leq X \leq 5.40) = .4970 + .3944$

$\qquad\qquad\qquad = .8914$ or 89.14%

(c) $P(5.20 \leq X \leq 6.10) = ?$

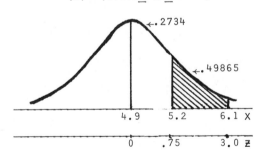

$Z = \dfrac{6.10 - 4.90}{.40} = \dfrac{1.20}{.40} = 3.00$

$Z = \dfrac{5.20 - 4.90}{.40} = \dfrac{.30}{.40} = .75$

$P(5.20 \leq X \leq 6.10) = .49865 - .2734$

$\qquad\qquad\qquad = .22525$ or 22.525%

(d) $P(X < 4.00) = ?$

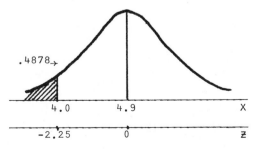

$Z = \dfrac{4.00 - 4.90}{.40} = \dfrac{-.90}{.40} = -2.25$

$P(X < 4.00) = .5000 - .4878$

$\qquad\qquad = .0122$ or 1.22%

(e) $P(X > 5.95) = ?$

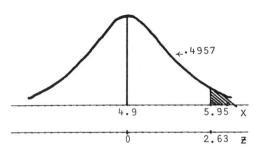

$$Z = \frac{5.95 - 4.90}{.40} = \frac{1.05}{.40} = 2.63$$

$$P(X > 5.95) = .5000 - .4957$$

$$= .0043 \text{ or } \underline{0.43\%}$$

(f) $P(X < 4.00 \text{ or } X > 5.95) = ?$

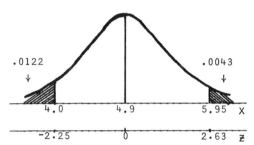

From parts (d) and (e)

$P(X < 4.00) = .0122$ and

$P(X > 5.95) = .0043$. Therefore,

$P(X < 4.00 \text{ or } X > 5.95) = .0122 + .0043$

$$= .0165 \text{ or } \underline{1.65\%}$$

(g) Computation of wage if only 10% of all workers earn more.

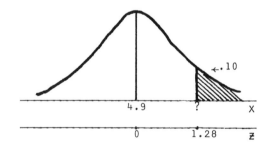

$$Z = \frac{X - \mu_X}{\sigma_X} \text{ or } 1.28 = \frac{X - 4.90}{.40}$$

$$X - 4.90 = 1.28(.40)$$

$$X = 4.90 + 1.28(.40)$$

$$X = 4.90 + .512 = \underline{\$5.412}.$$

(h) Computation of wage if only 25% of all workers earn less.

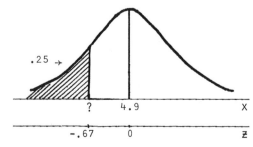

$$-.67 = \frac{X - 4.90}{.40}$$

$$X - 4.90 = -.67(.40)$$

$$X = 4.90 - .67(.40)$$

$$X = 4.90 - .268 = \underline{\$4.632}.$$

Note: $X = \$4.632$ may also be called the first quartile (Q_1).

REVIEW PROBLEMS

I.   Consider a very large community of families in which 5% of the house-
     holds have no children, 30% have one child, 35% have two children, 20%
     have three children and 10% have four children.

     (a) Set up the probability distribution of children per household in
         this community.

     (b) Compute the expected (average) number of children per household.

     (c) Compute the variance and standard deviation.

     (d) If a $750 tax exemption is permitted for each child, compute the
         amount of money that each family may be expected to deduct.

II. On any individual flight an airline serves one of three basic kinds of
     desserts--cake, ice cream and fruit. They serve cake one third of the
     time, ice cream one half of the time and fruit one sixth of the time.

     A. If 8 flights are randomly selected, find the probability that

         (1) two of the flights serve ice cream

(2) at least one of the flights serves ice cream.

B. If a random sample of 400 flights are selected, what is the probability that

(1) between 200 and 215 flights serve ice cream?

(2) at least 175 flights serve ice cream?

III. A clothing manufacturer purchases its cloth from the Baggins Woolen Firm. He notices that one brand of tweed cloth he uses to make suits has, on the average, one burr per 25 square yards of cloth. If it takes 10 square yards of cloth to make a suit, what is the probability that a suit

(a) will have no burrs?

(b) will have at least one burr?

(c) will have no more than two burrs?

IV. In a data processing center, a box containing 10 chips used to store statistical and financial programs has 2 defective chips. If a researcher selects 4 chips, what is the probability that

(a) exactly one is defective?

(b) none are defective?

V. An orange juice producer buys all his oranges from a large orange orchard. The amount of juice squeezed from these oranges is approximately normally distributed with a mean of 4.70 ounces and a standard deviation of .35 ounces. Find the proportion of oranges that can be squeezed to give

(a) between 4.70 and 5.30 ounces of juice

(b) between 4.15 and 5.60 ounces of juice

(c) between 3.95 and 4.10 ounces of juice

(d) less than 3.75 ounces of juice or more than 5.75 ounces of juice

(e) What is the amount of orange juice that can be squeezed if 84.13% of all oranges can be squeezed for more juice?

SOLUTIONS TO REVIEW PROBLEMS

I.

(a) Probability Distribution		(b) Expected Value	(c) Variance
Number of Children (X_i)	$P(X_i)$	$X_i \ P(X_i)$	$(X_i - \mu)^2 P(X_i)$
0	.05	.00	.20
1	.30	.30	.30
2	.35	.70	.00
3	.20	.60	.20
4	.10	.40	.40
	1.00	$\mu_X = 2.00$	$\sigma_X^2 = 1.10$

(d) $\sigma_X = \sqrt{\sigma_X^2} = \sqrt{1.1} = \underline{1.049}$.

(e) Amount each family may be expected to deduct is

$750 \times E(X) = \$750(2) = \underline{\$1,500}$.

II. A. Binomial Distribution: $P(X=x \mid n,p) = \dfrac{n!}{x!(n-x)!} \ p^x(1-p)^{n-x}$, where

n=8, p = .5, and X = number of flights that serve ice cream.

(1) $P(X=2) = \dfrac{8!}{2!6!} \ (.5)^2(.5)^6 = \underline{.1094}$.

(2) $P(X \geq 1) = 1 - P(X=0) = 1 - \dfrac{8!}{0!8!} \ (.5)^0(.5)^8 = 1 - .0039 = \underline{.9961}$.

B. Normal Approximation to Binomial: $\mu_X = np = 400(.5) = 200$,

$\sigma_X = \sqrt{np(1-p)} = \sqrt{400(.5)(.5)} = 10$.

(1) $Z \simeq \dfrac{X - np}{\sqrt{np(1-p)}} = \dfrac{215 - 200}{10} = \dfrac{15}{10} = 1.50$

$P(200 \leq X \leq 215) = \underline{.4332}$.

(2) $Z \simeq \dfrac{175 - 200}{10} = \dfrac{-25}{10} = -2.50$

$P(X \geq 175) = .4938 + .5000 = \underline{.9938}$.

III. Poisson Distribution: $P(X|\lambda) = \dfrac{e^{-\lambda}\lambda^{X}}{X!}$ where $\lambda = .40$ (i.e. $\dfrac{10}{25}$) burr per 10 square yards and X = number of burrs.

(a) $P(X=0 \mid \lambda=.40) = \dfrac{e^{-.40}(.40)^{0}}{0!} = \underline{.6703}$.

(b) $P(X \geq 1 \mid \lambda=.40) = 1 - P(x=0) = 1 - .6703 = \underline{.3297}$.

(c) $P(X \leq 2 \mid \lambda=.40) = P(X=0) + P(X=1) + P(X=2) = .6703 + \dfrac{e^{-.40}(.40)^{1}}{1!} +$

$\dfrac{e^{-.40}(.40)^{2}}{2!} = .6703 + .2681 + .0536 = \underline{.9920}$.

IV. Hypergeometric Distribution: $P(X \mid n, N, A) = \dfrac{\binom{A}{x}\binom{N-A}{n-x}}{\binom{N}{n}}$, where

$N = 10$, $A = 2$, $n = 4$, and X = number of defective chips.

(a) $P(X=1) = \dfrac{\binom{2}{1}\binom{8}{3}}{\binom{10}{4}} = \dfrac{2(56)}{210} = \underline{.5333}$.

(b) $P(X=0) = \dfrac{\binom{2}{0}\binom{8}{4}}{\binom{10}{4}} = \dfrac{70}{210} = \underline{.3333}$.

V. Normal Distribution: $\mu_X = 4.70$ ounces, $\sigma_X = .35$ ounces.

(a) $Z \simeq \dfrac{5.30 - 4.70}{.35} = \dfrac{.60}{.35} = 1.71$

$P(4.70 \leq X \leq 5.30) = \underline{.4564}$.

(b) $Z \simeq \dfrac{5.60 - 4.70}{.35} = \dfrac{.90}{.35} = 2.57$ $Z \simeq \dfrac{4.15 - 4.70}{.35} = \dfrac{-.55}{.35} = -1.57$

$P(4.15 \leq X \leq 5.60) = .4949 + .4418 = \underline{.9367}.$

(c) $Z \simeq \dfrac{3.95 - 4.70}{.35} = \dfrac{-.75}{.35} = -2.14$ $Z \simeq \dfrac{4.10 - 4.70}{.35} = \dfrac{-.60}{.35} = -1.71$

$P(3.95 \leq X \leq 4.10) = .4838 - .4564 = \underline{.0274}.$

(d) $Z \simeq \dfrac{5.75 - 4.70}{.35} = \dfrac{1.05}{.35} = 3.00$ $Z \simeq \dfrac{3.75 - 4.70}{.35} = \dfrac{-.95}{.35} = -2.71$

$P(X < 3.75 \text{ or } X > 5.75) = 1 - (.4966 + .49865) = \underline{.00475}.$

(e) $-1.00 = \dfrac{X - 4.70}{.35}$

$X - 4.70 = -1.00(.35)$

$X = 4.70 - 1.00(.35) = \underline{4.35 \text{ ounces}}.$

8 Sampling Distributions

One of the major goals of statistical analysis is to use a sample statistic such as the average to estimate a true population value. In order to be able to perform the analysis, we need to know the shape of the distribution of all possible samples. When the population is normally distributed, the sampling distribution of the mean will also be normally distributed with a variability that will decrease as the sample size becomes larger. On the other hand, if the population is "other than normally distributed," from the Central Limit Theorem we observe that once the sample size is large enough, the distribution of the sample mean will also follow a normal distribution.

MULTIPLE CHOICE

1. The "luncheon expense" vouchers of accounts of executives of a large advertising firm have a population mean of $12 per person and a population standard deviation of $4 per person. Are the following statements true or false?

   (a) 95.44% of all expense vouchers will be between $4 and $20.   T   F

   (b) If a random sample of 4 vouchers is selected, there is ap-   T   F
   proximately a 68.27% chance that the sample mean will be
   between $10 and $14.

   (c) If it is assumed that the expense vouchers are distributed   T   F
   symmetrically, there is approximately a 68.27% chance that
   a random sample of 16 selected vouchers will have a sample
   mean between $11 and $13.

(d) If a random sample of 64 expense vouchers is selected,   T   F
    there is a 95.44% chance that the sample mean will be
    between $11 and $13.

2. Which of the following is true regarding the sampling distribution of
   the mean for a large sample size?

   (a) It has the same shape, mean and standard deviation as the population.
   (b) It has a normal distribution with the same mean and standard devia-
       tion as the population.
   (c) It has the same shape and mean as the population, but has a smaller
       standard deviation.
   (d) It has a normal distribution with the same mean as the population
       but with a smaller standard deviation.

3. For samples of size 1, the sampling distribution of the mean will be
   normally distributed

   (a) regardless of the shape of the population.
   (b) if the shape of the population is symmetrical.
   (c) if the standard deviation of the population is known.
   (d) if the population is normally distributed.

4. If a population is normally distributed with μ_X=100 and σ_X=10 and a sample
   of 16 is selected, the proportion of sample means between 90 and 110 will
   _____ the proportion of individual values between 90 and 110.

   (a) be less than
   (b) be greater than
   (c) be the same as
   (d) not be comparable to

5. The standard error of the proportion will become larger

   (a) as p approaches 0.
   (b) as p approaches .50.
   (c) as p approaches 1.00.
   (d) as n increases.

EXAMPLES

I. The amount of time required for an oil and filter change in a service
    station is normally distributed with a mean of 45 minutes and a standard
    deviation of 10 minutes. What proportion of cars will be ready

    (a) between 45 and 52 minutes after they arrive at the station?
    (b) between 39 and 48 minutes after they arrive at the station?
    (c) If many random samples of 16 cars are selected, what would you
        expect the average and standard error of the mean to be?
    (d) What distribution would the sample means follow?
    (e) What proportion of the sample means would be between 45 and 52
        minutes?
    (f) What proportion of the sample means would be between 39 and 48
        minutes?
    (g) Compare the answers to parts (a) and (e), or (b) and (f) and explain
        the differences.

70

(h) If samples of 16 cars are selected, within what limits will 95% of the sample means fall?

(i) If samples of 16 cars are selected, what average time will be exceeded by 90% of the sample means?

(j) If the samples are selected from a population of 200 cars, find the standard error of the mean and the proportion of sample means between 45 and 52 minutes.

SOLUTION

Normal distribution of amount of time required for an oil and filter change in a station: μ_X= 45 minutes, σ_X= 10 minutes.

(a) $P(45 \leq X \leq 52)$ = ?

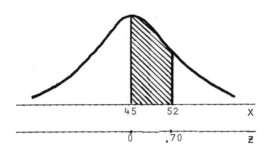

$$Z = \frac{X - \mu_X}{\sigma_X} = \frac{52 - 45}{10} = \frac{7}{10} = .70$$

$$P(45 \leq X \leq 52) = \underline{.2580}.$$

(b) $P(39 \leq X \leq 48)$ = ?

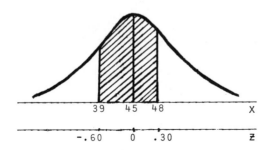

$$Z = \frac{39 - 45}{10} = \frac{-6}{10} = -.60$$

$$Z = \frac{48 - 45}{10} = \frac{3}{10} = .30$$

$$P(39 \leq X \leq 48) = .2257 + .1179$$

$$= \underline{.3436}.$$

(c) If many random samples of 16 cars are selected, the average of all the sample means $(\mu_{\bar{X}})$ is the population mean (μ_X), and the standard deviation of all the sample means $(\sigma_{\bar{X}})$ is the population standard deviation (σ_X) divided by the square root of the sample size. Therefore, $\mu_{\bar{X}} = \mu_X = 45$ minutes and $\sigma_{\bar{X}} = \sigma_X/\sqrt{n} = 10/\sqrt{16} = 2.5$ minutes.

(d) If the samples are selected from a normal population, the distribution of means follows a normal distribution, with mean, μ_X, and standard deviation, $\sigma_{\bar{X}} = \sigma_X/\sqrt{n}$.

(e) $P(45 \leq \bar{x} \leq 52) = ?$

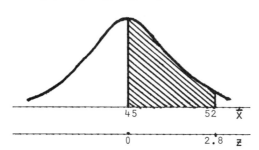

$$Z = \frac{\bar{x} - \mu_x}{\sigma_x/\sqrt{n}} = \frac{52 - 45}{10/\sqrt{16}} = \frac{7}{2.5} = 2.80$$

$$P(45 \leq \bar{x} \leq 52) = \underline{.4974}.$$

(f) $P(39 \leq \bar{x} \leq 48) = ?$

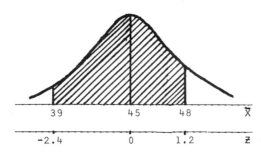

$$Z = \frac{39 - 45}{2.5} = \frac{-6}{2.5} = -2.40$$

$$Z = \frac{48 - 45}{2.5} = \frac{3}{2.5} = 1.20$$

$$P(39 \leq \bar{x} \leq 48) = .4918 + .3849$$
$$= \underline{.8767}.$$

(g) The proportion of cars that will be ready between 45 and 52 minutes (.2580) or between 39 and 48 minutes (.3436) after they arrive at the station is less than the proportion of sample means that would be between 45 and 52 (.4974) or between 39 and 48 (.8767), since the sample means are less variable than the population data itself (i.e. $\sigma_x = 10$, whereas $\sigma_{\bar{x}} = \sigma/\sqrt{n} = 2.5$).

(h) Limits within which 95% of the sample means will fall:

$$-Z_L = \frac{\bar{x}_L - \mu_x}{\sigma_x/\sqrt{n}} \quad \text{and} \quad Z_U = \frac{\bar{x}_U - \mu_x}{\sigma_x/\sqrt{n}} \qquad \text{Therefore,}$$

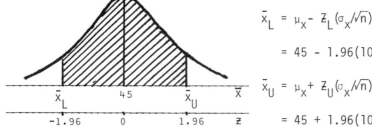

$$\bar{x}_L = \mu_x - Z_L(\sigma_x/\sqrt{n})$$
$$= 45 - 1.96(10/\sqrt{16}) = \underline{40.1}.$$

$$\bar{x}_U = \mu_x + Z_U(\sigma_x/\sqrt{n})$$
$$= 45 + 1.96(10/\sqrt{16}) = \underline{49.9}.$$

95% of all sample means of size 16 will fall between 40.1 and 49.9 minutes.

(i) Average time that will be exceeded by 90% of the sample means:

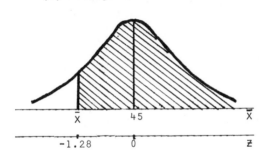

$$Z = \frac{\bar{X} - \mu_X}{\sigma_{\bar{X}}} \text{ or } -1.28 = \frac{\bar{X} - 45}{2.5}$$

$$\bar{X} = 45 - 1.28(2.5)$$

$$\bar{X} = 45 - 3.2 = \underline{41.8 \text{ minutes.}}$$

(j) Effect of the finite population correction factor on the standard error of the mean (σ_X = 10 minutes, N = 200, n = 16).

Without correction factor: $\sigma_{\bar{X}} = \sigma_X/\sqrt{n}$ = 2.5 minutes.

With correction factor: $\sigma_{\bar{X}} = \sigma_X/\sqrt{n} \sqrt{\frac{N - n}{N - 1}} = \frac{10}{\sqrt{16}} \sqrt{\frac{200 - 16}{200 - 1}}$

$$= 2.5\sqrt{.9246} = 2.5(.9616) = \underline{2.404 \text{ minutes.}}$$

In this example, the finite population correction factor reduced the previously computed standard error of the mean by about 4%. When the sample comprises an appreciable portion of the population (n/N > .05), the finite population correction factor must be taken into account when computing the standard error of the mean.

Computation of $P(45 \le \bar{X} \le 52)$ using $\sigma_{\bar{X}} = \sigma_X/\sqrt{n} \sqrt{\frac{N - n}{N - 1}}$

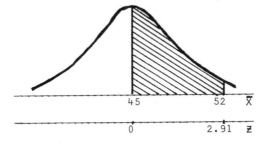

$$Z = \frac{\bar{X} - \mu_X}{\frac{\sigma_X}{\sqrt{n}}\sqrt{\frac{N - n}{N - 1}}} = \frac{52 - 45}{2.404} = 2.91$$

$$P(45 \le \bar{X} \le 52) = \underline{.4982.}$$

II. A car insurance company is concerned about the proportion of their policyholders involved in at least one vehicle collision within the past year. The records show that 10% of its policyholders were involved in at least one vehicle collision during the past year. If random samples of 400 policyholders are selected, what proportion of the samples will have

   (a) between 9% and 10% of its policyholders involved in at least one vehicle collision?

(b) less than 8% of its policyholders involved in at least one vehicle collision?
(c) Within what limits of the population percentage will 95% of the sample percentages fall?

SOLUTION

Sampling distribution of proportions is approximately normally distributed with mean = p = .10 and standard error of proportion,

$$\sigma_{p_S} = \sqrt{p(1-p)/n} = \sqrt{.10(.90)/400} = .015$$

(a) $P(.09 \leq p_S \leq .10)$ = ?

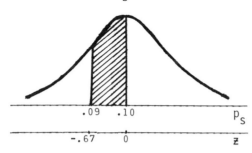

$$Z \approx \frac{p_S - p}{\sqrt{p(1-p)/n}} = \frac{.09 - .10}{.015}$$

$$= \frac{-.01}{.015} = -.67$$

$$P(.09 \leq p_S \leq .10) = \underline{.2486}.$$

(b) $P(p_S \leq .08)$ = ?

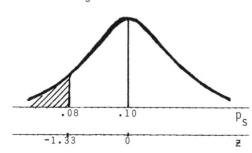

$$Z \approx \frac{.08 - .10}{.015} = \frac{-.02}{.015} = -1.33$$

$$P(p_S \leq .08) = .5000 - .4082 = \underline{.0918}.$$

(c) Limits within which 95% of the sample percentages will fall:

$$-Z_L \approx \frac{p_{S_L} - p}{\sqrt{p(1-p)/n}} \quad \text{and} \quad Z_U \approx \frac{p_{S_U} - p}{\sqrt{p(1-p)/n}}. \quad \text{Therefore,}$$

$$p_{S_L} = p - Z_L \sqrt{p(1-p)/n} = .10 - 1.96(.015) = \underline{.0706}.$$

$$p_{S_U} = p + Z_U \sqrt{p(1-p)/n} = .10 + 1.96(.015) = \underline{.1294}.$$

95% of all sample percentages will fall between 7.06% and 12.94%.

REVIEW PROBLEMS

I. The weekly amount of ink used by a particular magazine is approximately normally distributed with a mean of 12 gallons and a standard deviation of 2.7 gallons.

(a) For any given week, what is the probability that the magazine uses more than 11 gallons of ink?

(b) For any given week, what is the probability that the magazine uses between 12.9 and 13.4 gallons of ink?

(c) If many random samples of size 25 weeks are selected, what distribution would the sample means follow and what would you expect the average and standard error of the mean to be?

(d) What proportion of the sample means would be between 12.9 and 13.4 gallons of ink?

(e) What proportion of the sample means would be more than 11 gallons of ink?

(f) Within what limits around the true mean would 99% of the sample means fall?

II. The M & D Department Store is evaluating its lay-away plan. In the past, the proportion of customers who used the lay-away plan was .36. If random samples of 225 customers are selected, what proportion of samples will have

(a) between .36 and .45 of the customers using the lay-away plan?

(b) more than .40 of the customers using the lay-away plan?

(c) Within what limits of the population proportion will 98% of the sample proportions fall?

SOLUTIONS TO REVIEW PROBLEMS

I. (a) $Z = \dfrac{X - \mu_X}{\sigma_X} = \dfrac{11 - 12}{2.7} = -.37$

$P(x > 11) = .1443 + .5000 = \underline{.6443.}$

(b) $Z = \dfrac{13.4 - 12}{2.7} = .52$ $Z = \dfrac{12.9 - 12}{2.7} = .33$

$P(12.9 \le X \le 13.4) = .1985 - .1293 = \underline{.0692}.$

(c) In this example, the sample means follow a normal distribution with mean, $\mu_X = 12$ gallons, and a standard error of the mean, $\sigma_{\bar{X}} = 2.7/\sqrt{25} = .54$ gallons.

(d) $Z = \dfrac{\bar{x} - \mu_X}{\sigma_{\bar{X}}} = \dfrac{13.4 - 12}{.54} = 2.59$ $Z = \dfrac{12.9 - 12}{.54} = 1.67$

$P(12.9 \le \bar{x} \le 13.4) = .4952 - .4525 = \underline{.0427}.$

(e) $Z = \dfrac{11 - 12}{.54} = -1.85$

$P(\bar{x} > 11) = .4678 + .5000 = \underline{.9678}.$

(f) $-Z_L = \dfrac{\bar{x}_L - \mu_X}{\sigma_{\bar{X}}}$ and $Z_U = \dfrac{\bar{x}_U - \mu_X}{\sigma_{\bar{X}}}$

$\bar{x}_L = 12 - 2.58(.54) = \underline{10.6068 \text{ gallons}}.$

$\bar{x}_U = 12 + 2.58(.54) = \underline{13.3932 \text{ gallons}}.$

99% of the sample means will fall between 10.6068 and 13.3932 gallons.

II. (a) $Z \approx \dfrac{p_s - p}{\sqrt{p(1-p)/n}} = \dfrac{.45 - .36}{\sqrt{\dfrac{36(.64)}{225}}} = \dfrac{.09}{.032} = 2.81$

$P(.36 \le p_s \le .45) = \underline{.4975}.$

(b) $Z \approx \dfrac{.40 - .36}{.032} = 1.25$

$P(p_s > .40) = .5000 - .3944 = \underline{.1056}.$

(c) $p_{s_L} = .36 - 2.33(.032) = \underline{.2854}.$ $p_{s_U} = .36 + 2.33(.032) = \underline{.4346}.$

98% of the sample proportions will be between .2854 and .4346.

9 Estimation

In this chapter the concept of a sampling distribution is used to develop interval estimates of population parameters. The interval that is developed will vary depending on the value of the sample statistic. The level of confidence obtained refers to the probability that a sample correctly estimates the true value of the parameter in the population. The concept of a confidence interval is discussed for both quantitative data (means) and qualitative data (proportions). Moreover, the confidence interval estimation procedure is extended to determine the sample size necessary to achieve a desired level of confidence and sampling error. These procedures are also discussed for situations in which the samples are taken from finite populations.

MULTIPLE CHOICE

1. A random sample of 100 stores from a chain of 1,000 large department stores was selected to determine the number of lawnmowers sold at an end-of-season clearance sale. The sample results indicated an average of 6 and a standard deviation of 2 lawnmowers sold. A 95% confidence interval (5.623 to 6.377) was established on these results. Are the following statements true or false?

   (a) If the population would have consisted of 10,000 stores,   T   F
   the confidence interval estimate of the mean would have
   been wider in range.

   (b) Of all possible samples of 100 stores drawn from the pop-   T   F
   ulation of 1,000 stores, 95% of the sample means will
   fall between 5.623 and 6.377 lawnmowers.

(c) Of all possible samples of 100 stores drawn from the population of 1,000 stores, 95% of the confidence intervals developed will contain the true population mean within the interval.   T   F

(d) There are 10 possible samples of 100 stores that can be selected out of the population of 1,000 stores.   T   F

(e) 95% of the stores have sold between 5.623 and 6.377 lawnmowers.   T   F

(f) We do not know for sure whether the true population mean is between 5.623 and 6.377 lawnmowers sold.   T   F

2. The t distribution

(a) assumes the population is normally distributed.
(b) approaches the normal distribution as the sample size increases.
(c) has more area in the tails than the normal distribution.
(d) All of the above.

3. When determining the sample size for a mean for a given level of confidence and standard deviation, if the sampling error is allowed to increase the sample size required

(a) will increase.
(b) will decrease.
(c) will stay the same.
(d) cannot be determined.

4. The use of the finite population correction factor when determining sample size will

(a) have a larger effect for large populations.
(b) have a larger effect when sampling with replacement.
(c) decrease the sample size required.
(d) increase the sample size required.

5. If a survey is being designed that has several questions, the sample size required for the entire survey is based upon

(a) the smallest sample size required for any single question.
(b) the largest sample size required for any single question.
(c) the average sample size required for all the questions.
(d) the average of the smallest and largest sample sizes required for any one question.

EXAMPLES

I. A radio advertising agency would like to estimate the mean amount of time its audience spends listening to radio per day. What size sample is needed if the agency wants to have 99% confidence that its estimate is correct to within ± 10 minutes? From past studies, the standard deviation is estimated to be 150 minutes.

SOLUTION

Sample size determination for the mean: $n = \dfrac{Z^2 \sigma_X^2}{E^2}$

where

Z = confidence level desired = 2.58

E = sampling error permitted = ± 10 minutes

σ_X = standard deviation = 150 minutes.

Therefore,

$$n = \frac{(2.58)^2 (150)^2}{(10)^2} = \frac{(6.6564)(22,500)}{100} = 1,497.69 = \underline{1,498}.$$

II. A small utility company wishes to estimate the average amount of oil used by its 1,000 residential customers. Previous studies indicate that the standard deviation is 2 gallons. What size sample is required to be 98% confident of being correct to within ± .5 gallons?

SOLUTION

Sample size determination for means from a finite population

(N = 1,000, Z = 2.33, E = ± .5, and σ_X = 2)

(1) Compute sample size without regard to correction factor

$$n_0 = \frac{Z^2 \sigma_X^2}{E^2} = \frac{(2.33)^2 (2)^2}{(.5)^2} = \frac{(5.4289)(4)}{.25} = 86.8624.$$

(2) Correct for finite population

$$n = \frac{n_0 N}{n_0 + (N-1)} = \frac{86.8624 \,(1,000)}{86.8624 + (1,000 - 1)} = \frac{86,862.4}{1,085.8624} - \underline{80}.$$

III. A large shipment of air filters is received from the Riordan Supply Company. The air filters are to be sampled in order to estimate the proportion of unusable air filters. From past experience, the proportion of unusable filters is estimated to be .10. How large a random sample should be taken to estimate the true proportion of unusable air filters to be within ± .02 with 95% confidence?

SOLUTION

Sample size determination for proportion: $n = \dfrac{Z^2 p(1-p)}{E^2}$

where

Z = level of confidence desired = 1.96

E = sampling error permitted = $\pm$ .02

p = estimated true proportion of unusable air filters = .10.

$$n = \frac{(1.96)^2(.10)(.90)}{(.02)^2} = \frac{(3.8416)(.09)}{.0004} = 864.36 = \underline{864 \text{ filters}}.$$

IV. An audit test to establish the frequency of occurrence of failures to follow a specific internal control procedure was to be undertaken. The auditor decides that the maximum expected tolerable error rate to be anticipated is 5%. What size sample is required to achieve a sample precision of $\pm$ 2% with 99% confidence, if there are 10,000 documents to be sampled from?

SOLUTION

Sample size determination for proportion from a finite population

(N = 10,000, Z = 2.58, E = $\pm$ .02, and p = .05)

(1) Compute sample size without regard to correction factor

$$n_0 = \frac{Z^2 p(1-p)}{E^2} = \frac{(2.58)^2(.05)(.95)}{(.02)^2} = \frac{(6.6564)(.0475)}{.0004} = 790.4475.$$

(2) Correct for finite population

$$n = \frac{n_0 N}{n_0 + (N-1)} = \frac{790.4475(10,000)}{790.4475 + (10,000 - 1)} = \frac{7,904,475}{10,789,4475} = \underline{733}.$$

V. The accounting department of the Ace Department Store is interested in the average amount of its delinquent accounts. A random sample of 25 delinquent accounts discloses an average of $15.50 and a standard deviation of $2.50.

(a) Find the 95% confidence interval estimate of the true average amount owed to the store.

(b) If the department store has 100 delinquent accounts, find the 95% confidence interval estimate of the true average amount owed to the store.

SOLUTION

(a) Confidence interval estimate for the mean (σ_x unknown and we assume the sample comes from a normal population):

$$\bar{x} \pm t_{n-1} \frac{S}{\sqrt{n}}$$

where

$$\bar{x} = \$15.50 \qquad\qquad n = 25$$
$$S = \$2.50 \qquad\qquad t_{24} = 2.064$$

$$\$15.50 \pm (2.064) \frac{2.50}{\sqrt{25}} = 15.50 \pm (2.064)(.5) = 15.50 \pm 1.032$$

$$\$14.468 \leq \mu_x \leq \$16.532.$$

(b) Confidence interval estimate for the mean from a finite population (N = 100). We use the finite correction factor since n/N > 5%.

$$\bar{x} \pm t_{n-1} \frac{S}{\sqrt{n}} \sqrt{\frac{N-n}{N-1}}$$

$$\$15.50 \pm (2.064) \frac{2.50}{\sqrt{25}} \sqrt{\frac{100-25}{100-1}} = 15.50 \pm (2.064)(.5)(\sqrt{.7576})$$

$$15.50 \pm (2.064)(.5)(.8704) = 15.50 \pm (2.064)(.4352) = 15.50 \pm .90$$

$$\$14.60 \leq \mu_x \leq \$16.40.$$

VI. A research analyst for an energy conservation group is interested in the proportion of air conditioners that have an energy efficiency ratio of at least 8. He takes a random sample of 400 owners of air conditioners and finds that 240 own air conditioners with energy efficiency ratios of at least 8. Find the 95% confidence interval estimate of the true proportion of air conditioners that have an energy efficiency ratio of at least 8.

SOLUTION

Confidence interval estimate for the population proportion:

$$p_s \pm Z \sqrt{\frac{p_s(1-p_s)}{n}}$$

$$p_s = \frac{X}{n} = \frac{240}{400} = .6 \qquad Z = 1.96$$

$$.6 \pm 1.96 \sqrt{\frac{.6(.4)}{400}} = .6 \pm 1.96 \, (\sqrt{.0006})$$

$$.6 \pm 1.96 \, (.0245) = .6 \pm .048$$

$$.552 \leq p \leq .648$$

VII. A small metropolitan area has both a morning and evening newspaper. A random sample of 360 out of 4,000 households are selected and it is found that 54 of the 360 households selected read both the morning and evening papers. Construct the 99% confidence interval estimate for the true proportion of households that read both the morning and evening newspapers.

SOLUTION

Confidence interval estimate for the population proportion from a finite population (N = 4,000) using the finite population correction factor since n/N > 5%:

$$p_s \pm Z \sqrt{\frac{p_s(1-p_s)}{n}} \sqrt{\frac{N-n}{N-1}}$$

$$p_s = \frac{54}{360} = .15 \qquad Z = 2.58$$

$$.15 \pm 2.58 \sqrt{\frac{.15(.85)}{360}} \sqrt{\frac{4,000-360}{4,000-1}}$$

$$.15 \pm 2.58 \, (.0188)(.9541) = .15 \pm 2.58 \, (.0179) = .15 \pm .0462$$

$$.1038 \leq p \leq .1962$$

83

REVIEW PROBLEMS

I. The Tinker Toy Company accountant wants to estimate the mean value of infant toys in inventory.

   (a) If the standard deviation is known to be $10 and the desired sampling error for the true mean is ± $1.25 with 95% confidence, find the required sample size needed.

   (b) If there are only 1,000 infant toys to be sampled from, what then is the required sample size?

II. The Department of Labor is interested in estimating the proportion of steel companies with employees belonging to a national labor union.

   (a) How large a sample will be required if the sampling error is not to exceed ± 5% with 95% confidence?

   (b) How large should the sample be if there are 1,500 steel companies?

III.   An auditor takes a random sample of 16 inventory items from a popu-
        lation of 2,000 and finds that the mean dollar value of errors in
        the sample is $3.55 with a standard deviation of $1.50.

        (a) Find the 95% confidence interval estimate for the true mean
            error amount.

        (b) Assuming that the $1.50 is the population standard deviation,
            find the 95% confidence interval estimate for the true mean.

IV. A random sample of 100 items is taken from a continuous production operation and 10 items are found to be broken.

(a) Find the 95% confidence interval estimate for the true proportion of broken items.

(b) If each production operation consists of 1,000 items, find the 95% confidence interval estimate of the true proportion of broken items.

SOLUTIONS TO REVIEW PROBLEMS

I. (a) $\sigma_X = \$10$; $E = \pm \$1.25$; $Z = 1.96$.

$$n = \frac{Z^2 \sigma_X^2}{E^2} = \frac{(1.96)^2 (10)^2}{(1.25)^2} = 245.8624 = 246.$$

(b) $\sigma_X = \$10$; $E = \pm \$1.25$; $Z = 1.96$; $N = 1,000$.

From part (a): $n_0 = 245.8624$

$$n = \frac{n_0 N}{n_0 + (N-1)} = \frac{245.8624\ (1,000)}{245.8624 + (1,000 - 1)} = \frac{245,862.4}{1,244.8624} = 198.$$

II. (a) $E = \pm .05$; $Z = 1.96$; assume $p = .50$ when p is not given, since this will give the maximum sample size n for a given E and Z.

$$n = \frac{Z^2 p(1-p)}{E^2} = \frac{(1.96)^2(.5)(.5)}{(.05)^2} = 384.16 = 385.$$

(b) $E = \pm\ .05;\ Z = 1.96;\ N = 1,500;$ assume $p = .50$ when p is not given.

From part (a): $n_0 = 384.16$

$$n = \frac{n_0 N}{n_0 + (N-1)} = \frac{384.16\ (1,500)}{384.16 + (1,500 - 1)} = \frac{576,240}{1,883.16} = 306.$$

III.(a) $N = 2,000;\ n = 16;\ \bar{x} = \$3.55;\ S = \$1.50;$ and $t_{15} = 2.1315.$

Since $\dfrac{n}{N} = \dfrac{16}{2,000} = .008 < 5\%,$ we ignore the finite correction factor.

$$\bar{x} \pm t_{n-1} \frac{S}{\sqrt{n}} = 3.55 \pm (2.1315) \frac{1.50}{\sqrt{16}} = 3.55 \pm .7993$$

$$\$2.7507 \leq \mu_x \leq \$4.3493$$

(b) If we have a population standard deviation (σ_x known) and we make the assumption that the sample came from a normal population, the confidence interval estimate for the true mean is

$$\bar{x} \pm Z \frac{\sigma_x}{\sqrt{n}}$$

$$\$3.55 \pm 1.96\ (1.50\ /\sqrt{16}) = \$3.55 \pm 1.96(.375) = \$3.55 \pm .735$$

$$\$2.815 \leq \mu_x \leq \$4.285$$

IV. (a) $p_s = \dfrac{10}{100} = .10;\ Z = 1.96.$

$$p_s \pm Z \sqrt{\frac{p_s(1-p_s)}{n}} = .10 \pm 1.96 \sqrt{\frac{(.10)(.90)}{100}} = .10 \pm .0588$$

$$.0412 \leq p \leq .1588$$

(b) $N = 1,000;\ p_s = .10;\ Z = 1.96.$

$$p_s \pm Z \sqrt{\frac{p_s(1-p_s)}{n}} \sqrt{\frac{N-n}{N-1}} = .10 \pm 1.96 \sqrt{\frac{(.10)(.90)}{100}} \sqrt{\frac{1,000 - 100}{1,000 - 1}}$$

$$.10 \pm 1.96\ (.02847) = .10 \pm .0558$$

$$.0442 \leq p \leq .1558$$

87

Hypothesis Testing I: Introduction and Concepts

10

In this chapter the concepts of sampling distributions and statistical inference are utilized to develop statistical hypothesis testing procedures. These methods enable decisions to be made concerning the value of a parameter (such as a mean or a proportion) based only on sample evidence. In making these decisions, two types of risk are involved. The Type I error α (the level of significance) represents the probability of erroneously concluding that the null hypothesis is false. The Type II error β represents the probability of not rejecting the null hypothesis when it is false. The concept of the power of a test $(1-\beta)$ is developed and the effect of varying the sample size, the level of significance and the type of test on power is also considered.

MULTIPLE CHOICE

1. If a test of hypothesis has a Type I (α) error of .01, we mean

    (a) if the null hypothesis is true, we don't reject it 1% of the time.
    (b) if the null hypothesis is true, we reject it 1% of the time.
    (c) if the null hypothesis is false, we don't reject it 1% of the time.
    (d) if the null hypothesis is false, we reject it 1% of the time.

2. If the Type I error for a given test is to be decreased, then for a fixed sample size

    (a) the Type II (β) error will also decrease.
    (b) the Type II (β) error will increase.
    (c) the power of the test will increase.
    (d) a one-tailed test must be utilized.

3. If a market researcher wanted to determine whether at least 20% of consumers would purchase a particular product

   (a) either a one-tailed or a two-tailed test could be used with equivalent results.
   (b) a one-tailed test should be utilized.
   (c) a two-tailed test should be utilized.
   (d) None of the above.

4. A one sample test for a proportion is being performed. If the critical value is +2.33 and the test statistic is +1.37,

   (a) the null hypothesis should not be rejected.
   (b) the alternative hypothesis cannot be rejected.
   (c) the null hypothesis should be rejected.
   (d) None of the above.

5. For a given sample size, if the level of significance (α) is increased, the power of the test

   (a) will increase.   (c) will remain the same.
   (b) will decrease.   (d) cannot be determined.

6. P-value is the probability of obtaining a particular result or one even more extreme--if the null hypothesis were true. When testing the hypothesis H_0: μ = 16 against the alternative hypothesis H_1: $\mu \neq$ 16, the computed Z value is 2.00. For this problem the P-value is

   (a) .0228.   (c) .01135.
   (b) .0456.   (d) not determined.

7. P-value is the probability of obtaining a particular result or one even more extreme--if the null hypothesis were true. When testing the hypothesis H_0: p = .20 against the alternative hypothesis H_1: p > .20, the computed Z value is 1.50. For this problem the P-value is

   (a) .0668.   (c) .1336.
   (b) .0334.   (d) not determined.

8. P-value is the probability of obtaining a particular result or one even more extreme--if the null hypothesis were true. When testing the hypothesis H_0: μ = 20 against the alternative hypothesis H_1: $\mu <$ 20, the computed t value is -2.35. The sample size is 15. For this problem the P-value is

   (a) between .01 and .025.   (c) between .005 and .0125.
   (b) between .02 and .05.   (d) not determined.

9. A Type I error (α) is commited when

   (a) we reject a null hypothesis that is true
   (b) we don't reject a null hypothesis that is true
   (c) we reject a null hypothesis that is false.
   (d) we don't reject a null hypothesis that is false

10. A Type II error (β) is committed when

    (a) we reject a null hypothesis that is true
    (b) we don't reject a null hypothesis that is true
    (c) we reject a null hypothesis that is false
    (d) we don't reject a null hypothesis that is false

11. An experimenter would be justified in using a level of significance of $\alpha = .10$ or higher when

    (a) a Type II error is much more costly than a Type I error
    (b) a Type I error is much more costly than a Type II error
    (c) only α levels of $\alpha = .05$ or $\alpha = .01$ are ever justified. Thus, an α of .10 or higher should never be used.
    (d) none of the above.

12. To determine the sample size for the mean, we must know

    (a) the confidence level desired Z
    (b) the sampling error permitted, E
    (c) the standard deviation, σ_X
    (d) all of the above

EXAMPLES

I.   A quality control expert is called in to determine whether a newly installed machine is producing a particular cotton cloth according to the specifications set by the manufacturer. The mean warp-breaking strength of this particular cotton cloth has been established to be 66 pounds. A random sample of 36 pieces of cotton cloth is obtained from a production run on this machine. The results of the sample reveal a mean warp-breaking strength of 64.5 pounds and a standard deviation of 5 pounds. Can the quality control expert say that the cotton cloth produced on the new machine meets the warp-breaking specification of the manufacturer at the .05 level of significance?

SOLUTION

Hypothesis test for mean of one sample (σ unknown).

1. H_0: $\mu_X = 66$ pounds (i.e. The mean warp-breaking strength of a particular cotton cloth is 66 pounds.)

2. H_1: $\mu_X \neq 66$ pounds (i.e. The mean warp-breaking strength of a particular cotton cloth is not 66 pounds.)

3. $\alpha = .05$.

4. n = 36 pieces of cloth.

5. Decision rule:

Reject H_0 Don't Reject H_0 Reject H_0

.025   .025

-2.03 0 2.03
t_{35} t_{35}

Reject H_0 if $t_{35} > 2.03$ or if $t_{35} <$

-2.03. Otherwise, don't reject H_0.

6. Sample results:

$\bar{x}$ = 64.5 pounds, S = 5 pounds, n = 36.

7. Test statistic:

$$t_{n-1} = \frac{\bar{x} - \mu_x}{S/\sqrt{n}} = \frac{64.5 - 66}{5/\sqrt{36}} = \frac{-1.5}{.8333} = -1.80.$$

8. Conclusion:

Since t_{35} = -1.80 > $t_{35,.025}$ = -2.03, we cannot reject H_0.

There is no evidence that the newly installed machine is not turning out cotton cloth that meets the specifications of the manufacturer.

II. A director of personnel claims that 40 percent of all systems analysts employed by the banks switch jobs within two years after they are hired. If a random sample of 200 systems analysts selected indicates that 96 of them switched jobs, can the claim be rejected at the .05 level of significance?

SOLUTION

Hypothesis test for proportion of one sample.

1. H_0: p = .40 (i.e. The percent of systems analysts who switch jobs within two years after they are hired is 40.)

2. H_1: p ≠ .40 (i.e. The percent of systems analysts who switch jobs within two years after they are hired is not 40).

3. α = .05.

4. Decision rule:

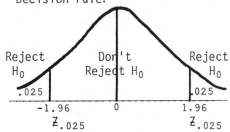

Reject H_0 Don't Reject H_0 Reject H_0

.025   .025

-1.96   0   1.96

$Z_{.025}$ $Z_{.025}$

Reject H_0 if $Z_{.025}$ > 1.96 or $Z_{.025}$ < -1.96. Otherwise, don't reject H_0.

5. Sample results:

$$p_s = \frac{x}{n} = \frac{96}{200} = .48.$$

6. Test statistic:

$$Z \approx \frac{p_s - p}{\sqrt{\frac{p(1-p)}{n}}} = \frac{.48 - .40}{\sqrt{\frac{(.40)(.60)}{200}}} = \frac{.08}{\sqrt{.0012}} = \frac{.08}{.03464} = 2.31.$$

7. Conclusion:

Since $Z = 2.31 > Z_{.025} = 1.96$, reject H_0.

The conclusion at the .05 level of significance is that the percent of systems analysts who switch jobs within two years after they are hired is above 40 percent.

III. The Food and Drug Administration has decided that if a particular food product has more than 8 grams of impurities it should be banned. From previous studies on this food product, the standard deviation was found to be 1.5 grams. A random sample of 36 of these food items is selected. The Food and Drug Administration is willing to have a 5% risk that the food product will be banned when the impurities measure 8 grams or less.

(a) Compute the probability of banning the food product when it has an average of 8.4 grams of impurities.

(b) Compute the probability of banning the food product when it has an average of 8.9 grams of impurities.

(c) If the Food and Drug Administration wishes to have a 99% chance of banning the food product when it has an average of 8.9 grams of impurities, what sample size should be selected?

SOLUTION

This is an example of finding the power of the test $(1 - \beta)$--the probability of banning the food product for differing values of the true average impurities in the particular food product.

H_0: $\mu_0 \leq 8$ grams
(Don't ban food product).

H_1: $\mu_1 > 8$ grams
(Ban food product).

$\alpha = .05$ (risk).

$n = 36$, $\sigma_X = 1.5$ grams.

$\bar{X} = \mu_0 + Z \dfrac{\sigma_X}{\sqrt{n}} = 8 + 1.645 \dfrac{1.5}{\sqrt{36}}$

$\bar{X} = 8 + .41125 = 8.41125.$

Decision Rule:

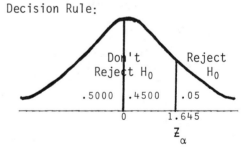

Reject H_0 if $\bar{X} > 8.41125$. Otherwise, don't reject H_0.

(a) Power $= 1 - \beta = P(\text{ban food product when } \mu_1 = 8.4)$

$= P(\bar{X} > 8.41125 \text{ when } \mu_1 = 8.4) = ?$

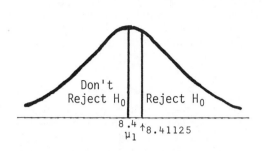

$$Z = \frac{\bar{x} - \mu_x}{\sigma_x/\sqrt{n}} = \frac{8.41125 - 8.4}{1.5/\sqrt{36}}$$

$$= \frac{.01125}{.25} = .05.$$

Power = $P(\bar{x} > 8.41125$ when $\mu_1 = 8.4)$

$= P(\bar{x} > 8.41125) = .5000 - .0199$

$= \underline{.4801}.$

(b) Power = $1 - \beta = P($ban food product when $\mu_1 = 8.9)$

$= P(\bar{x} > 8.41125$ when $\mu_1 = 8.9) = ?$

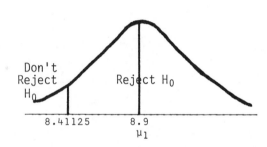

$$Z = \frac{8.41125 - 8.9}{1.5/\sqrt{36}} = \frac{-.48875}{.25} = -1.96.$$

Power = $P(\bar{x} > 8.41125$ when $\mu_1 = 8.9)$

$= .5000 + .4750 = \underline{.9750}.$

(c) Sample size based on α and β risks.

$$n = \frac{\sigma_x^2(Z_\alpha - Z_\beta)^2}{(\mu_0 - \mu_1)^2}$$

where

σ_x^2 = the variance of the population = $(1.5)^2 = 2.25$

Z_α = Z value for a given α level of significance (.05) = 1.645

Z_β = Z value for a given β risk of a Type II error (.01)= -2.33

μ_0 = value of the population mean under the null hypothesis = 8 grams

μ_1 = value of the population mean under the alternative hypothesis = 8.9 grams.

Don't Reject H_0 ↓ **Reject H_0**

.01   .4900   .5000

-2.33   0

Z_β

$$n = \frac{2.25 \, (1.645 - (-2.33))^2}{(8 - 8.9)^2}$$

$$n = \frac{2.25 \, (3.975)^2}{(-.9)^2} = \frac{2.25(15.800625)}{.81}$$

$$n = 43.89 = \underline{44}.$$

Thus, a sample of size 44 items of a particular food product would be required if the Food and Drug Administration is willing to have a 5% risk of making a Type I error and a 99% chance of rejecting the null hypothesis of 8 grams and detecting that the true average of impurities has increased to 8.9 grams.

REVIEW PROBLEMS

I.   A manufacturer of detergent claims that the mean weight of a particular size box of detergent is 20 ounces and that no more than 12% of the boxes weigh less than 19.75 ounces. A random sample of 64 boxes is selected and the mean weight is 19.9 ounces with a standard deviation of .14 ounces. In addition, there were 12 boxes of detergent with weights less than 19.75 ounces. (Use α = .05 in the following problems.)

(a) Is there evidence regarding the validity of the manufacturer's claim that the mean weight is 20 ounces?

(b) Is there evidence regarding the validity of the manufacturer's claim that no more than 12% of the boxes of detergent weigh less than 19.75 ounces?

II. The president of a mail order health food outfit is given the opportunity to acquire the exclusive rights to market a wonder drug called Vitamin X. Based upon the cost of production of this drug and the profit to be made, the president has decided that if there is evidence that the average order per household would be more than 150 capsules he would acquire the exclusive rights to market Vitamin X. If no evidence can be demonstrated he would not acquire the exclusive rights. Based on previous experience with similar type vitamins, the standard deviation was 32 capsules. He mails out capsules to 64 randomly selected households on his mailing list. He is willing to take a 1% risk that he will acquire the exclusive rights to market Vitamin X when the average order is at most 150 capsules.

(a) Compute the probability of acquiring the exclusive rights to market Vitamin X when the average order is 156 capsules.

(b) Compute the probability of acquiring the exclusive rights to market Vitamin X when the average order is 165 capsules.

(c) If the president wishes to have a 95% chance of acquiring the exclusive rights to market Vitamin X when the population average order is 165 capsules, what sample size should he select?

SOLUTIONS TO REVIEW PROBLEMS

I.   (a) H_0: μ_X = 20 ounces (Mean weight is 20 ounces).

         H_1: $\mu_X \neq$ 20 ounces (Mean weight is not 20 ounces).

         α = .05.

         Decision rule: Reject H_0 if t_{63} < -1.9983 or if t_{63} > 1.9983.
                         Otherwise, don't reject H_0.

Sample results: $\bar{x} = 19.9$ ounces, $S = .14$ ounces, $n = 64$.

Test statistic: $t_{63} = \dfrac{\bar{x} - \mu_x}{S/\sqrt{n}} = \dfrac{19.9 - 20}{.14/\sqrt{64}} = \dfrac{-.10}{.0175} = -5.71.$

Conclusion: At the .05 level of significance reject H_0 since $t_{63} = -5.71 < -1.9983$. The manufacturer's claim that the mean weight is 20 ounces is invalid.

(b) H_0: $p \leq .12$ (No more than 12% of the boxes weigh less than 19.75).
H_1: $p > .12$ (More than 12% of the boxes weigh less than 19.75).
$\alpha = .05$.

Decision rule: Reject H_0 if $Z > 1.645$. Otherwise, don't reject H_0.

Sample results: $p_S = \dfrac{x}{n} = \dfrac{12}{64} = .1875.$

Test statistic: $Z \approx \dfrac{p_S - p}{\sqrt{\dfrac{p(1-p)}{n}}} = \dfrac{.1875 - .12}{\sqrt{\dfrac{.12(.88)}{64}}} = \dfrac{.0675}{.0406} = 1.663.$

Conclusion: At the .05 level of significance reject H_0 since $Z = 1.663 > 1.645$. There is evidence that more than 12% of the detergent boxes weigh less than 19.75 ounces.

II. H_0: $\mu_x \leq 150$ capsules (Don't buy exclusive rights for Vitamin X).
H_1: $\mu_x > 150$ capsules (Buy exclusive marketing rights for Vitamin X).
$\alpha = .01$. $\bar{x} = 150 + 2.33\,(32/\sqrt{64})$
$n = 64$, $\sigma = 32$ capsules. $\bar{x} = 150 + 9.32 = 159.32$.
Decision rule: Reject H_0 if $\bar{x} > 159.32$. Otherwise don't reject H_0.

(a) $Z = \dfrac{159.32 - 156}{32/\sqrt{64}} = \dfrac{3.32}{4} = .83.$

P(buy exclusive rights when $\mu_1 = 156$) = P($\bar{x} > 159.32$ when $\mu_1 = 156$)
= .5000 - .2967 = <u>.2033</u>.

(b) $Z = \dfrac{159.32 - 165}{32/\sqrt{64}} = \dfrac{-5.68}{4} = -1.42.$

P(buy exclusive rights when $\mu_1 = 165$) = P($\bar{x} > 159.32$ when $\mu_1 = 165$)
= .4222 + .5000 = <u>.9222</u>.

(c) $n = \dfrac{\sigma^2 (Z_\alpha - Z_\beta)^2}{(\mu_0 - \mu_1)^2} = \dfrac{(32)^2 (2.33 - (-1.645))^2}{(150 - 165)^2} = \underline{72}.$

Hypothesis Testing II: Differences Between Quantitative Variables

11

In this chapter we shall extend our hypothesis testing concepts to additional procedures which are concerned with differences between quantitative variables. The difference between the means of two groups will be evaluated for both independent and related samples. Moreover, when the samples are independent, t-tests with and without the assumption of homogeneity of population variances are developed. In addition, the F-test for the equality of two population variances is considered.

MULTIPLE CHOICE

1. If we are testing for the difference between the means of two independent samples with samples of $n_1 = 15$ and $n_2 = 20$, the number of degrees of freedom is equal to ___ provided that we can assume that the population variances are equal.

    (a) 20   (c) 33
    (b) 35   (d) 19

2. If we are testing for the difference between the means of two independent samples with sample standard deviations of $S_1 = 4$ and $S_2 = 10$ and sample sizes $n_1 = 16$ and $n_2 = 20$, the number of degrees of freedom is equal to

    (a) 27.43.   (c) 34.29.
    (b) 36.   (d) 34.

3. The t test for the difference between the means of two independent samples assumes that

   (a) the sample sizes are equal.
   (b) the sample variances are equal.
   (c) the population variances are equal.
   (d) All of the above.

4. A test for the difference between two variances can be performed using the

   (a) t distribution.   (c) F distribution
   (b) normal distribution.   (d) None of the above.

5. P-value is the probability of obtaining a particular result or one even more extreme--if the null hypothesis were true. When testing the hypothesis $H_0: \sigma_1^2 = \sigma_2^2$ against the alternative hypothesis $H_1: \sigma_1^2 > \sigma_2^2$, the computed F value is 3.00. The sample sizes are $n_1 = 10$ and $n_2 = 16$. For this problem the P-value is

   (a) between .05 and .10.   (c) between .0125 and .025.
   (b) between .025 and .05.   (d) not determined.

EXAMPLES

I. The president of a national retail outlet wishes to examine some characteristics of its sales force assigned to four regional offices. The data are presented below:

	Regional Offices			
	NorthEast (NE)	SouthEast (SE)	NorthWest (NW)	SouthWest (SW)
Sample size of Sales Force (n)	64	25	16	50
Average number of years employed ($\bar{X}$)	9.6 years	10.3 years	10.2 years	7.9 years
Standard deviation of number of years employed (S)	2.1 years	2.0 years	1.9 years	2.0 years

For each of the following problems use a .01 level of significance to determine:

(a) whether there are any differences in the mean number of years employed by the firm for sales personnel in the NorthEast and South-West regional offices?

(b) whether there are any differences in the variances in years employed by the firm for sales personnel in the SouthEast versus NorthWest regional offices?

SOLUTION

(a) Testing for the difference between the means of two populations—independent samples (assuming the variances are equal).

1. $H_0: \mu_{NE} = \mu_{SW}$ (There is no difference in the mean number of years employed by the firm for sales personnel in the two regional offices.).

2. $H_1: \mu_{NE} \neq \mu_{SW}$ (There is a difference in the mean number of years employed by the firm for sales personnel in the two regional offices.).

3. $\alpha = .01$.

4. Decision rule:

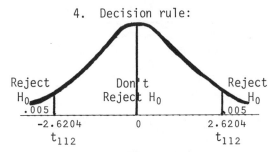

Reject H_0 if $t_{112} > 2.6204$ or $t_{112} < -2.6204$. Otherwise, don't reject H_0.
(Note: df $= n_{NE} + n_{SW} - 2$
$= 64 + 50 - 2 = 112$.)

5. Sample results:

NorthEast: $\bar{x}_{NE} = 9.6$ years; $S_{NE} = 2.1$ years; $n_{NE} = 64$.

SouthWest: $\bar{x}_{SW} = 7.9$ years; $S_{SW} = 2.0$ years; $n_{SW} = 50$.

6. Test statistic:

$$t_{n_{NE} + n_{SW} - 2} = \frac{\bar{x}_{NE} - \bar{x}_{SW}}{\sqrt{S_p^2 \left(\frac{1}{n_{NE}} + \frac{1}{n_{SW}} \right)}}$$

where $S_p^2 = \frac{(n_{NE}-1)S_{NE}^2 + (n_{SW}-1)S_{SW}^2}{n_{NE} + n_{SW} - 2}$

$$S_p^2 = \frac{(64-1)(2.1)^2 + (50-1)(2)^2}{64 + 50 - 2} = \frac{277.83 + 196}{112} = 4.230625.$$

99

$$t_{112} = \frac{9.6 - 7.9}{\sqrt{4.230625\left(\frac{1}{64} + \frac{1}{50}\right)}} = \frac{1.7}{\sqrt{4.230625}\ (.035625)}$$

$$= \frac{1.7}{\sqrt{.150716}} = \frac{1.7}{.3882} = 4.38.$$

7. Conclusion: Since $t_{112} = 4.38 > t_{.005,112} = 2.6204$, reject H_0.

The sample difference between the NorthEast and SouthWest regional offices is much larger than what could have occurred by chance if the two populations had equal means. Therefore, there is a significant difference in the average number of years employed by the firm for sales personnel in the NorthEast and SouthWest regional offices at the .01 level of significance.

(b) Hypothesis test for the equality of variances from two populations (assume samples from normal populations).

1. H_0: $\sigma_{SE}^2 = \sigma_{NW}^2$.

2. H_1: $\sigma_{SE}^2 \neq \sigma_{NW}^2$.

3. $\alpha = .01$.

4. Decision rule:

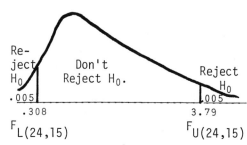

Reject H_0 if $F_{(24,15)} > 3.79$ or

$F_{(24,15)} < .308$. Otherwise, don't reject H_0.

Note: $F_{L(a,b)} = \dfrac{1}{F_{U(b,a)}}$

where a = number of degrees of freedom of group A = $n_A - 1$; and

b = number of degrees of freedom of group B = $n_B - 1$.

5. Sample results:

$S_{SE} = 2.0$ years.

$n_{SE} = 25.$

$S_{NW} = 1.9$ years.

$n_{NW} = 16.$

$F_{L(24,15)} = \dfrac{1}{F_{U(15,24)}} = \dfrac{1}{3.25} = .308.$

6. Test statistic:

$$F_{(n_{SE}-1),(n_{NW}-1)} = F_{(24,15)} = \frac{S_{SE}^2}{S_{NW}^2} = \frac{(2.0)^2}{(1.9)^2} = \frac{4.00}{3.61} = 1.11.$$

7. Conclusion: Since $F_{(24,15)} = 1.11$ falls in the don't reject region, do not reject H_0. There is no evidence that there is a difference in the variances in the years employed by the firm for sales personnel in the SouthEast and NorthWest regional offices. The sample difference may be attributed to chance at the .01 level of significance.

II. The following are the results of a test given to eight sets of twins-- one member of each set is taught a foreign language by Method A and the other member of the set is taught by Method B. Are there differences in the two methods at the .05 level of significance?

Set of Twins	#1	#2	#3	#4	#5	#6	#7	#8
Method A	87	96	68	72	91	64	87	79
Method B	83	89	75	74	83	68	76	70

SOLUTION

The paired difference t-test for related samples (assume samples from normal populations).

1. H_0: $\mu_d = 0$ (There is no difference in the two methods.)

2. H_1: $\mu_d \neq 0$ (There is a difference in the two methods.)

3. $\alpha = .05$.

4. Decision rule:

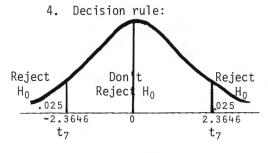

Reject H_0 if $t_7 > 2.3646$ or if $t_7 < -2.3646$. Otherwise, don't reject H_0.

5. Sample results:

Set of Twins	Method A	Method B	$d_i = X_{A_i} - X_{B_i}$	d_i^2
1	87	83	4	16
2	96	89	7	49
3	68	75	-7	49
4	72	74	-2	4
5	91	83	8	64
6	64	68	-4	16
7	87	76	11	121
8	79	70	9	81
			$\sum_{i=1}^{8} d_i = 26$	$\sum_{i=1}^{8} d_i^2 = 400$

$\bar{d} = 3.25.$

$$S_d = \sqrt{\frac{n \sum_{i=1}^{n} d_i^2 - \left(\sum_{i=1}^{n} d\right)^2}{n(n-1)}} = \sqrt{\frac{8(400)-(26)^2}{8(7)}} = \sqrt{45.07143} = 6.7135.$$

6. Test statistic:

$$t_7 = \frac{\bar{d} - 0}{S_d/\sqrt{n}} = \frac{3.25}{6.7135/\sqrt{8}} = \frac{3.25}{2.3736} = 1.37.$$

7. Conclusion: At the .05 level of significance we cannot reject H_0 since $t_7 = 1.37 < t_{7, \alpha/2 = .025} = 2.3646$. There is no evidence that the two methods used for teaching a foreign language are significantly different.

REVIEW PROBLEMS

I. The Hobbit Firm hired two salesmen six months ago. Now an opportunity for advancement has occurred and only one of them may be selected. The sales records will be used as criteria for selection. A random sample of 121 sales records for salesman A showed average sales of $4,500 with standard deviation of $900 and the number of sales made was 95. A random sample of 121 sales records for salesman B showed average sales of $4,250 with a standard deviation of $850 and the number of sales made was 85.

(a) Do the two sales records differ significantly with respect to average sales? (Use .05 level of significance.)

(b) Is there a difference in the variances between Salesman A and Salesman B? (Use .05 level of significance.)

II. A statistics professor would like to determine whether students in her class showed improved performance on the final examination as compared to the midterm examination. A random sample of 7 students selected from a large class revealed the following midterm and final examination scores:

Student	#1	#2	#3	#4	#5	#6	#7
Midterm	70	62	57	68	89	63	82
Final	80	79	87	88	85	79	91

Is there a significant improvement on the final examination? (Use α = .01.)

SOLUTIONS TO REVIEW PROBLEMS

I.   (a) H_0: $\mu_A = \mu_B$ (i.e. $\mu_A - \mu_B = 0.$)

H_1: $\mu_A \neq \mu_B$ (i.e. $\mu_A - \mu_B \neq 0.$)

$\alpha = .05$.   (Assume equal variances in the two populations.)

Decision rule: Reject H_0 if $t_{240} > 1.96$ or if $t_{240} < -1.96$.

Otherwise, don't reject H_0.

Sample results and test statistic:

$\bar{x}_A = \$4,500$; $S_A = \$900$; $n_A = 121$;

$\bar{x}_B = \$4,250$; $S_B = \$850$; $n_B = 121$.

$$S_p^2 = \frac{(n_A-1)S_A^2 + (n_B-1)S_B^2}{n_A + n_B - 2} = \frac{120(900)^2 + 120(850)^2}{240} = 766,250.$$

$$t_{240} = \frac{\bar{x}_A - \bar{x}_B}{\sqrt{S_p^2(\frac{1}{n_A} + \frac{1}{n_B})}} = \frac{4,500 - 4,250}{\sqrt{766,250(\frac{1}{121} + \frac{1}{121})}} = \frac{250}{112.54} = 2.22.$$

Conclusion: At the .05 level of significance we would reject H_0 since $t_{240} = 2.22 > 1.96$. There is a significant difference between the two salesmen with respect to average sales. Salesman A should be promoted over Salesman B.

(b) H_0: $\sigma_A^2 = \sigma_B^2$

H_1: $\sigma_A^2 \neq \sigma_B^2$

$\alpha = .05$.

Decision rule: Reject H_0 if $F_{(120,120)} < .70$ or if $F_{(120,120)} > 1.43$.

Otherwise, don't reject H_0.

$$F_{(120,120)} = \frac{S_A^2}{S_B^2} = \frac{(900)^2}{(850)^2} = 1.12.$$

Conclusion: Since $F_{(120,120)}$ = 1.12 falls in the don't reject H_o region, there is no evidence that there is a difference in the variances between salesmen A and B.

II. $H_o: \mu_d \leq 0$ $\qquad\qquad$ Decision rule: Reject H_o if t_6 > 3.1427.

$H_1: \mu_d > 0$ $\qquad\qquad\qquad\qquad$ Otherwise, don't reject H_o.

α = .01.

Student	#1	#2	#3	#4	#5	#6	#7
Midterm	70	62	57	68	89	63	82
Final	80	79	87	88	85	79	91
d_i = Final − Midterm	10	17	30	20	-4	16	9

$$\Sigma d_i = 98; \ \Sigma d_i^2 = (10)^2 + (17)^2 + \ldots + (9)^2 = 2,042.$$

$$\bar{d} = \frac{\Sigma d_i}{n} = \frac{98}{7} = 14; \ S_d = \sqrt{\frac{n\Sigma d_i^2 - (\Sigma d_i)^2}{n(n-1)}} = \sqrt{\frac{7(2,042)-(98)^2}{7(6)}}$$

$$= 10.5672$$

$$t_6 = \frac{\bar{d}}{S_d/\sqrt{n}} = \frac{14}{10.5672/2.6458} = 3.51.$$

Conclusion: Since t_6 = 3.51 > $t_{\alpha=.01}$ = 3.1427 reject H_o. There is evidence that there is a significant improvement on the final as compared to the midterm examination at the .01 level of significance.

Hypothesis Testing III: Differences Between Proportions and Other Chi-Square Tests

This chapter focuses primarily on tests for proportions and various chi-square methods. For qualitative data and independent samples, a test for the difference between two proportions is developed using two methods--the normal approximation and the chi-square technique. In addition, when dealing with related samples the McNemar test for the difference between two proportions is described. Moreover, in this chapter, several tests based on chi-square are discussed. The chi-square test is extended to the case of more than two groups and generalized as a test of independence between two qualitative variables. Furthermore, the chi-square test is also utilized to determine the goodness of fit of a set of data to a specific probability distribution. Finally, the one-sample (chi-square) test for the variance in the population is considered.

MULTIPLE CHOICE

1. A test for the difference between two proportions can be performed using the

   (a) t distribution.   (c) F distribution.
   (b) chi-square distribution. (d) All of the above.

2. The number of degrees of freedom in a contingency table that has 4 rows and 3 columns when performing a chi-Square test is equal to

   (a) 12.   (c) 1.
   (b) 5.   (d) 6.

3. Which of the following statistical tests follow a chi-Square distribution?

   (a) test for a variance
   (b) test of goodness of fit
   (c) test for the difference between two proportions
   (d) All of the above.

4. P-value is the probability of obtaining a particular result or one even more extreme--if the null hypothesis were true. When testing the hypothesis H_0: σ_X^2 = 50 against the alternative hypothesis H_1: σ_X^2 > 50, the computed χ^2 value is 22.22. The sample size is 15. For this problem the P-value is

   (a) between .025 and .05.   (c) between .05 and .10.
   (b) between .10 and .20.   (d) not determined.

EXAMPLES

I. The president of a cosmetic firm plans to test market a new line of
    perfume in a large metropolitan area. She divides this area into four
    equally divided sales regions. After the first week of intensive adver-
    tising, the following number of orders by sales regions is tabulated:

Sales Regions	Number of Orders
NorthEast	35
Central	28
South	25
West	32
Total	120

Will the new line of perfume do equally well in the four sales regions
at the .05 level of significance?

SOLUTION

I. H_0: The new line of perfume will do equally well in the sales regions.

    H_1: The new line of perfume will not do equally well in the regions.

    $\alpha = .05$. Decision rule: Reject H_0 if $\chi_3^2 > 7.815$. Otherwise, don't
                     reject H_0.

Sales Region	f_0	f_T	(f_0-f_T)	$(f_0-f_T)^2$	$\dfrac{(f_0-f_T)^2}{f_T}$
NorthEast	35	30	5	25	.833
Central	28	30	-2	4	.133
South	25	30	-5	25	.833
West	32	30	2	4	.133
	120	120			$\chi_3^2 = 1.932$

Conclusion: Since $\chi_3^2 = 1.932 < \chi_{\alpha=.05}^2 = 7.815$ do not reject H_0.

There is no evidence that the new line of perfume will not do
equally well in the sales regions at the .05 level of significance.

II. The president of a national retail outlet wishes to examine some characteristics of its sales force assigned to four regional offices. The
data are presented below:

	Regional Offices			
	North East (NE)	South East (SE)	North West (NW)	South West (SW)
Sample size of sales force (n)	64	25	16	50
Average number of years employed $(\bar{x})$	9.6 years	10.3 years	10.2 years	7.9 years
Standard deviation of number of years employed (s)	2.1 years	2.0 years	1.9 years	2.0 years
Number of sales personnel in sample with MBAs (x)	16	12	5	20

For each of the following problems use a .01 level of significance to
determine:

(a) whether there are any differences between the proportions of sales
personnel in the NE and SW regional offices who have MBA degrees?

(b) whether there is any justification to the claim that in the North-
East regional office the true standard deviation of the number of
years employed by the firm is 2.0 years?

SOLUTION

(a) Chi-Square test for the difference between two proportions.

1. H_0: $P_{NE} = P_{SW}$ (There is no difference in the proportion of
sales personnel with MBAs in the two regional
offices.).

2. H_1: $P_{NE} \neq P_{SW}$ (There is a difference in the proportion of
sales personnel with MBAs in the two regional
offices.).

3. $\alpha = .01$.

4. Decision rule:

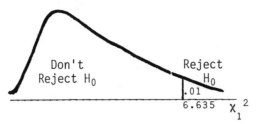

Reject H_0 if $\chi_1^2 > 6.635$. Otherwise, don't reject H_0.

5. Sample results:

Degree	Regional Office		Totals
	NorthEast	SouthWest	
Have MBA	16 {20.2105}	20 {15.7895}	36
No MBA	48 {43.7895}	30 {34.2105}	78
Totals	64	50	114

{ } Bracketed numbers are theoretical frequencies.

110

6. Test statistic:

$$\chi^2_{(R-1)(C-1)} \approx \sum_{\text{all cells}} \frac{(f_0 - f_T)^2}{f_T}$$

where f_0 = observed frequency in each cell

f_T = theoretical frequency in each cell = $\dfrac{n_r n_c}{n}$

where n_r = total number in row

n_c = total number in column

n = total sample size

R = number of rows in the contingency table

C = number of columns in the contingency table

$(R-1)(C-1)$ = number of degrees of freedom. (Note: The degrees of freedom for a test of C proportions is actually $C-1$.)

$$f_T = \frac{36(64)}{114} = 20.2105 \qquad f_T = \frac{36(50)}{114} = 15.7895$$

$$f_T = \frac{78(64)}{114} = 43.7895 \qquad f_T = \frac{78(50)}{114} = 34.2105$$

f_0	f_T	(f_0-f_T)	$(f_0-f_T)^2$	$\dfrac{(f_0-f_T)^2}{f_T}$
16	20.2105	-4.2105	17.72831025	.8772
48	43.7895	4.2105	17.72831025	.4049
20	15.7895	4.2105	17.72831025	1.1228
30	34.2105	-4.2105	17.72831025	.5182

$$\chi^2_1 = 2.9231$$

7. Conclusion: Since $\chi^2_1 = 2.9231 < \chi^2_{.01,1} = 6.635$, do not reject H_0. There is no evidence of a significant difference between the proportions of sales personnel assigned to the two regional offices who have MBA degrees.

(b) Hypothesis test for a population variance (assume sample from a normal population).

1. H_0: σ_{NE} = 2.0 years (or σ_{NE}^2 = 4.0).

2. H_1: σ_{NE} ≠ 2.0 years (or σ_{NE}^2 ≠ 4.0).

3. α = .01.

4. Decision rule:

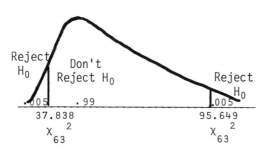

Reject H_0 if χ_{63}^2 < 37.838 or

χ_{63}^2 > 95.649.   Otherwise, don't

reject H_0.

(Note: df = n-1 = 64-1 = 63.)

5. Sample results:

S = 2.1 years; n = 64.

6. Test statistic:

$$\chi_{63}^2 = \frac{(n-1)S^2}{\sigma_X^2} = \frac{(64-1)(2.1)^2}{(2)^2} = \frac{63(4.41)}{4} = 69.46.$$

7. Conclusion: Do not reject H_0 since χ_{63}^2 = 69.46 falls in the don't reject region. There is no evidence that the standard deviation of the number of years employed by the firm in the NorthEast regional office is not 2.0 years at the .01 level of significance.

III. The administrator of a large computer center has collected data on the number of times that service to users has been interrupted (usually due to mechanical failure) per day over the past 1,000 days.

Interruptions/Day	Number of Days
0	320
1	350
2	172
3	82
4	36
5	24
6	16
	1,000

Does the distribution of service interruptions come from a Poisson distribution at the .05 level of significance?

SOLUTION

Chi-Square goodness of fit test for a Poisson distribution.

1. H_0: The interruptions per day follows a Poisson distribution.

2. H_1: The interruptions per day follows a probability distribution other than a Poisson distribution.

3. $\alpha = .05$.

4. Decision rule:

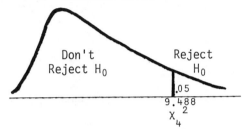

Reject H_0 if $x_4^2 > 9.488$. Otherwise, don't reject H_0.

Don't Reject H_0

Reject H_0

.05
9.488
x_4^2

5. Sample results:

Interruptions Per Day (X_j)	Number of Days (f_j)	$X_j f_j$	Poisson Probability $P(X_j$ given $\mu_X=1.3)$	Theoretical Frequency $f_T=nP(X_j)$
0	320	0	.2725	272.5
1	350	350	.3543	354.3
2	172	344	.2303	230.3
3	82	246	.0998	99.8
4	36	144	.0324	32.4
5	24	120	.0084	8.4
6	16	96	.0018	1.8
7 or more	0	0	.0005	.5
Totals	1,000	1,300	1.0000	1,000.0

$$\bar{X} = \frac{\sum_{j=1}^{K} X_j f_j}{n} = \frac{1,300}{1,000} = 1.3.$$

6. Test statistic:

$$X_{K-p-1}^2 \approx \sum_K \frac{(f_0 - f_T)^2}{f_T}$$

where f_0 = the observed frequency

f_T = the theoretical frequency

113

K = the number of categories or classes that remain after collapsing classes = 6

p = the number of parameters estimated from the data = 1 (i.e. estimate of mean of Poisson distribution)

K-p-1 = the degrees of freedom = 4.

Interruptions Per Day	f_0	f_T	(f_0-f_T)	$(f_0-f_T)^2$	$\dfrac{(f_0-f_T)^2}{f_T}$
0	320	272.5	47.5	2,256.25	8.280
1	350	354.3	-4.3	18.49	.052
2	172	230.3	-58.3	3,398.89	14.759
3	82	99.8	-17.8	316.84	3.175
4	36	32.4	3.6	12.96	.400
5 or more	40	10.7	29.3	858.49	80.233

$$\chi_4^2 = 106.899$$

7. Conclusion: Since $\chi_4^2 = 106.899 > \chi_{.05,4}^2 = 9.488$ reject H_0.

The administrator of a large computer center must conclude that the distribution of the number of service interruptions per day does not follow a Poisson distribution.

IV. Fleischman, Berenson, and Levine wanted to know whether this study guide and workbook was meeting the needs of students. A random sample of 500 students were selected and they indicated their expectations prior to their purchase and their satisfaction at the completion of the semester. The results were as follows:

Expectation prior to Purchase	Satisfaction after Completion of Coursework		
	Satisfied	Unsatisfied	Totals
Positive expectation	349	1	350
Negative expectation	148	2	150
	497	3	500

Determine whether the proportion of students who are satisfied after the completion of coursework is greater than the proportion of students who had positive expectations before purchasing the study guide and workbook (use $\alpha = .05$).

SOLUTION

We use the McNemar test:

H_0: $P_1 \geq P_2$

H_1: $P_1 < P_2$

The critical value would be -1.645. Our decision rule is to reject H_0 if $\bar{Z} < -1.645$, otherwise we will not reject H_0.

For our data:

A = 349

B = 1

C = 148

D = 2

and the sample proportion of students with positive expectations (p_{s_1}) and satisfied "customers" (p_{s_2}) are:

$$p_{s_1} = \frac{A + B}{n} = \frac{349+1}{500} = .700$$

$$p_{s_2} = \frac{A + C}{n} = \frac{349+148}{500} = .994$$

Test statistic:

$$\bar{Z} = \frac{B - C}{\sqrt{B + C}} = \frac{1 - 148}{\sqrt{1 + 148}} = \frac{-147}{\sqrt{149}} = \frac{-147}{12.21} = -12.04$$

Since $\bar{Z}$ = 12.04 < -1.645 we reject the null hypothesis and conclude that the proportion of students with positive expectations prior to the purchase of the study guide and workbook is less than the proportion of satisfied "customers" at term's end!

REVIEW PROBLEM

I. The Hobbit firm hired two salesmen six months ago. Now an opportunity for advancement has occurred and only one of them may be selected. The sales record will be used as criteria for selection. A random sample of 121 sales records for salesman A showed average sales of $4,500 with a standard deviation of $900 and the number of sales made was 95. A random sample of 121 sales records for salesman B showed average sales of $4,250 with a standard deviation of $850 and the nunber of sales made was 85.

(a) Do the two sales records differ significantly with regard to percentage of sales? (Use .05 level of significance.)

(b) Is the standard deviation of sales of salesman B equal to $840? (Use .05 level of significance.)

SOLUTION TO REVIEW PROBLEM

(a) H_0: $p_A = p_B$

H_1: $p_A \neq p_B$

$\alpha = .05$.

Decision rule: Reject H_0 if $Z > 1.96$ or if $Z < -1.96$. Otherwise, don't reject H_0.

Sample results and test statistic:

$$p_{s_A} = \frac{x_A}{n_A} = \frac{95}{121} = .7851; \quad p_{s_B} = \frac{x_B}{n_B} = \frac{85}{121} = .7025.$$

$$\bar{p} = \frac{x_A + x_B}{n_A + n_B} = \frac{95 + 85}{121 + 121} = .7438.$$

$$Z \approx \frac{\left(p_{s_A} - p_{s_B}\right) - \left(p_A - p_B\right)}{\sqrt{\bar{p}(1-\bar{p})\left(\frac{1}{n_A} + \frac{1}{n_B}\right)}} = \frac{(.7851 - .7025)-0}{\sqrt{.7438(.2562)\left(\frac{1}{121} + \frac{1}{121}\right)}} = 1.47.$$

Conclusion: Since $Z = 1.47 < Z_{.025} = 1.96$ do not reject H_0. There is no evidence that there is a significant difference between the two salesmen with respect to percentage of sales. (Note: An alternate test would be the Chi-Square test for two proportions since $\chi^2_1 = Z^2$).

(b) H_0: $\sigma_B = \$840$.   Decision rule: Reject H_0 if $\chi_{120}^2 > 152.211$

   H_1: $\sigma_B \neq \$840$.   or if $\chi_{120}^2 < 91.573$. Otherwise,

   $\alpha = .05$.   don't reject H_0.

$$\chi_{120}^2 = \frac{(n_B-1)S_B^2}{\sigma_B^2} = \frac{(121-1)(850)^2}{(840)^2} = 122.874.$$

Conclusion: Since $\chi_{.025}^2 = 91.573 < \chi_{120}^2 = 122.874 < \chi_{.975}^2 =$ 152.211, do not reject H_0. There is no evidence that the standard deviation of sales for salesman B is not $840.

13 Bayesian Decision Making

In the last several chapters we have investigated a decision making methodology that is usually called the classical approach. In this chapter we discuss an alternative methodology that directly takes into account the subjective or prior probability of various events. A table of all possible events and all possible alternative courses of action, called the payoff table, is developed. Various criteria for arriving at the optimal decision, such as expected monetary value and expected opportunity loss, are then considered.

MULTIPLE CHOICE

1. The decisions arrived at by using the expected monetary value and expected opportunity loss criteria

   (a) will always be the same.
   (b) will never be the same.
   (c) sometimes will be the same and other times will be different.
   (d) are not comparable.

2. The optimal decision using the expected monetary value criteria is to choose the alternative course of action that has

   (a) the largest possible payoff for an event.
   (b) the largest expected profit.
   (c) the smallest expected profit.
   (d) the smallest expected utility.

3. The number of different alternative courses of action is _____ the number of different events or states of the world.

   (a) always smaller than
   (b) always equal to
   (c) always larger than
   (d) sometimes smaller than and other times larger than

4. The utility curve for an individual who places a smaller value on increasing amounts of profit is called

   (a) risk averter.   (c) risk neutral.
   (b) risk seeker.   (d) All of the above.

5. If the opportunity loss for action j and event i is zero, then

   (a) this action will result in a profit of $0.
   (b) this action is optimal for the particular event.
   (c) this action will be optimal for all events.
   (d) this action will have an expected opportunity loss of 0.

EXAMPLE

A group of foreign investors are interested in investing $500,000 in one of three investments which are affected by the price of gold for a period of one year. The investment alternatives are (1) Gold, (2) Dollars and (3) Securities. The return (in ten thousands of dollars) for each investment versus the fluctuation of gold prices during the year is as follows:

Fluctuation of Gold Prices (E_i)	Investment Alternatives		
	Gold	Dollars	Securities
Up	$ 16	$ -2	$ -10
Same	-6	-1	20
Down	4	5	6

Based on past experience, the foreign investors assign the following probabilities for the price of gold during the year:

Fluctuation of Gold Prices (E_i)	Probability (P_i)
Up	.55
Same	.30
Down	.15
	1.00

120

(a) Using the expected monetary value (EMV) criterion, determine what investment the foreign investors should make.

(b) Determine the expected value of perfect information (EVPI) and interpret its meaning.

(c) Set up the opportunity loss table.

(d) Compute the expected opportunity loss (EOL).

(e) Before making a final decision, the foreign investors are considering acquiring an economic forecast for the forthcoming year. Based on past forecasts, when the price of gold has gone up, the probability of a good economic forecast was .80; when the price of gold has stayed the same, the probability of a good forecast was .50; when the price of gold has gone down the probability of a good economic forecast was .24. If the forecast indicates a bad economy, revise the prior probability in the light of this new information.

(f) Use the revised probabilities obtained in part (e) of this example along with the expected monetary value criterion to determine what the foreign investors should invest in.

SOLUTION

(a) Decision on what investment the foreign investors should make using the expected monetary value (EMV) criterion. (Remember the return is in ten thousands of dollars.)

Expected Profit Table

Fluctuation of Gold Prices (E_i)	Prior Probability (P_i)	Investment Alternatives		
		Gold (A_1)	Dollars (A_2)	Securities (A_3)
Up	.55	($16)(.55) = $8.80	(-$2)(.55) = -$1.10	(-$10)(.55) = -$5.50
Same	.30	(-6)(.30) = -1.80	(-1)(.30) = -.30	(20)(.30) = 6.00
Down	.15	(4)(.15) = .60	(5)(.15) = .75	(6)(.15) = .90
	1.00	$7.60 EMV (A_1)	-$.65 EMV (A_2)	$1.40 EMV (A_3)

↑
Optimal Act

(Note: $EMV(A_j) = \sum_{i=1}^{3} X_{ij} P_i$

The optimal decision is for the foreign investors to invest in gold.

(b) Computation of expected value of perfect information.

Fluctuation of Gold Prices (E_i)	Prior Probability (P_i)	Profit Table Investment Alternatives			Profit Under Certainty	Expected Profit Under Certainty
		Gold	Dollars	Securities		
Up	.55	$16	-$2	-$10	$16	$16(.55) = 8.80
Same	.30	-6	-1	20	20	20(.30) = 6.00
Down	.15	4	5	6	6	6(.15) = .90
	1.00					$15.70

EVPI = Expected Profit Under Certainty minus Expected Monetary Value of Optimal Act = $15.70 - 7.60 = $8.10 (ten thousands) or $81,000.

The foreign investors would be willing to pay at most $81,000 for obtaining perfect information.

(c) Setup of opportunity loss table.

Fluctuation of Gold Prices (E_i)	Optimum Action	Profit of Optimum Action	Opportunity Loss Investment Alternatives		
			Gold	Dollars	Securities
Up	Gold	$16	$16-16 = $0	$16-(-2) = $18	$16-(-10) = $26
Same	Securities	20	20-(-6) = 26	20-(-1) = 21	20 - 20 = 0
Down	Securities	6	6 - 4 = 2	6 - 5 = 1	6 - 6 = 0

(d) Computation of expected opportunity loss (EOL) for each investment alternative.

Fluctuation of Gold Prices (E_i)	Prior Probability (P_i)	OPPORTUNITY LOSS Investment Alternatives			EXPECTED OPPORTUNITY LOSS Investment Alternatives		
		Gold	Dollars	Securities	Gold (A_1)	Dollars (A_2)	Securities (A_3)
Up	.55	$0	$18	$ 26	0(.55) = $0	18(.55) = $9.90	26(.55) = $14.30
Same	.30	26	21	0	26(.30) = 7.80	21(.30) = 6.30	0(.30) = 0
Down	.15	2	1	0	2(.15) = .30	1(.15) = .15	0(.15) = 0
	1.00				$8.10 EOL ($A_1$)	$16.35 EOL ($A_2$)	$14.30 EOL ($A_3$)

↑
Optimal Act

$$EOL(A_j) = \sum_{i=1}^{3} \ell_{ij} P_i$$

The optimal action for the foreign investors is to invest in gold.

Note: The expected opportunity loss of the optimal action (minimum EOL) is equal to the expected value of perfect information.

(e) Revision of prior probabilities in light of new information.

123

(e)

Fluctuation of Gold Prices (E_i)	Prior Probability (P_i)	Conditional Probability $P(\text{Bad Forecast}\|E_i)$	Joint Probability $P_i \times P(\text{Bad Forecast}\|E_i)$	Revised Prior Probability* $P(E_i\|\text{Bad Forecast})$
Up	.55	.2	$(.55)(.2) = .11$	$\dfrac{.11}{.374} = .294$
Same	.30	.5	$(.30)(.5) = .15$	$\dfrac{.15}{.374} = .401$
Down	.15	.76	$(.15)(.76) = .114$	$\dfrac{.114}{.374} = .305$
	1.00		.374	1.000

$\sum\limits_{i=1}^{3} P_i \times P(\text{Bad Forecast}\|E_i) = .374.$

* Revised prior probability obtained by applying Bayes' Theorem:

$$P(E_j|\text{Bad Forecast}) = \frac{\text{Joint Probability}}{\text{Sum of Joint Probabilities}} = \frac{P(E_j \text{ and Bad Forecast})}{P(\text{Bad Forecast})}$$

$$= \frac{P_i \times P(\text{Bad Forecast}|E_i)}{\sum\limits_{i=1}^{3} P_i \times P(\text{Bad Forecast}|E_i)}$$

Example: $P(\text{Down}|\text{Bad Forecast}) = \dfrac{(.15)(.76)}{(.55)(.2)+(.30)(.5)+(.15)(.76)} = \dfrac{.114}{.374} = .305.$

(f) Decision on what to invest using revised prior probabilities when the forecast is bad and the expected monetary value criterion.

Fluctuation of Gold Prices (E_i)	Revised Probability (P_i)	Profit Table Investment Alternatives			Expected Profit Table Investment Alternatives		
		Gold	Dollars	Securities	Gold	Dollars	Securities
Up	.294	$16	-$2	-$10	$4.70	-$.59	-$2.94
Same	.401	-6	-1	20	-2.41	-.40	8.02
Down	.305	4	5	6	1.22	1.53	1.83
	1.000				$3.51	$ .54	$6.91

Optimal Act

In this case, the optimal act is for the foreign investors to invest in securities since on average $69,100 could be expected as compared to a profit of $35,100 and $5,400 if they invested in gold and dollars, respectively.

125

REVIEW PROBLEM

I. The E. Leet Car-Rental Firm is interested in determining the number of cars to have available for daily rental. The firm realizes a net profit of $40 for each car rented. When there is a demand for a car and none are available the goodwill cost is $10. An unused car (one that is not rented) represents a cost of $5. The firm has gathered the following information on the daily demand for cars:

Daily Demand (e_i)	Probability (P_i)
50	.14
100	.50
150	.30
200	.06
	1.00

(a) Determine the optimal number of cars that the firm should have available using the expected monetary value (EMV) criterion.

(b) Determine the expected value of perfect information and interpret
    its meaning.

(c) Set up and compute the opportunity loss and expected opportunity
    loss (EOL) tables.

(d) The owner of the E. Leet Car-Rental Firm notices that the level of demand is dependent on the weather. Therefore, prior to making a final decision on the number of cars to have available daily he wants to see if he should hire a meteorologist. Based on past experience, when 50 cars are demanded, the probability of a "fair" forecast is .60 (rainy is .40); when 100 cars are demanded, the probability of a fair forecast is .75; when 150 cars are demanded, the probability of a fair forecast is .78; when 200 cars are demanded, the probability of a fair forecast is .55. If the forecast says fair, revise the prior probabilities in light of this new information.

(e) Use the revised probabilities obtained in part (d) of this problem along with the expected monetary value criterion to determine the optimal number of cars the firm should have available.

SOLUTION TO REVIEW PROBLEMS

(a)   Profit and Expected Profit Table

Daily Demand (e_i)	P_i	Profits* Alternatives (A_j)				Expected Profits** Alternatives (A_j)			
		50	100	150	200	50	100	150	200
50	.14	$2,000	$1,750	$1,500	$1,250	$ 280	$ 245	$ 210	$ 175
100	.50	1,500	4,000	3,750	3,500	750	2,000	1,875	1,750
150	.30	1,000	3,500	6,000	5,750	300	1,050	1,800	1,725
200	.06	500	3,000	5,500	8,000	30	180	330	480
	1.00					$1,360	$3,475	$4,215	$4,130

↑
Optimal Act

*Given: Net profit $40 for each car rented.
　　　　Cost $5 for each unused car.
　　　　Goodwill cost $10 for each time demand for a car not met.

Profit = $40e_i - $5(A_j - e_i)$ if $A_j \geq e_i$ (i.e. supply ≥ demand).
  or
Profit = $40A_j + $10(A_j - e_i)$ if $A_j < e_i$ (i.e. supply < demand).

　Example: Looking at profits for $A_2 = 100$, the computations are as follows:
　when $e_1 = 50$ Profit = $40e_1 - 5(A_2 - e_1) = 40(50) - 5(100-50) = $1,750.

　　　　$e_2 = 100$ Profit = $40e_2 - 5(A_2 - e_2) = 40(100) - 5(100-100) = 4,000.

　　　　$e_3 = 150$ Profit = $40A_2 + 10(A_2 - e_3) = 40(100) + 10(100-150) = 3,500.

　　　　$e_4 = 200$ Profit = $40A_2 + 10(A_2 - e_4) = 40(100) + 10(100-200) = 3,000.

**EMV $(A_j) = \sum_{i=1}^{4} X_{ij} P_i$

　Example: EMV $(A_2) = $1,750(.14) + 4,000(.50) + 3,500(.30) + 3,000(.06)$

　　　　　　　　$= $245 + 2,000 + 1,050 + 180 = $3,475.

Conclusion: The car-rental firm should have 150 cars available each day.

(b)   Expected Profit for Perfect Information Table

Daily Demand (e_i)	P_i	Optimum Action	Profit Under Certainty	Expected Profit Under Certainty
50	.14	$A_1 = 50$	$ 2,000	$ 280
100	.50	$A_2 = 100$	4,000	2,000
150	.30	$A_3 = 150$	6,000	1,800
200	.06	$A_4 = 200$	8,000	480
	1.00			$4,560

EVPI = Expected Profit Under Certainty - EMV(Optimum Act) =
$4,560 - $4,215 = $345.

The E. Leet Car-Rental Firm would be willing to spend at most $345 to obtain perfect information.

(c)   Opportunity Loss and Expected Opportunity Loss Table

Daily Demand (e_i)	P_i	Opportunity Loss Alternatives (A_j)				Expected Opportunity Loss* Alternatives (A_j)			
		50	100	150	200	50	100	150	200
50	.14	$ 0	$ 250	$ 500	$ 750	$ 0	$ 35	$ 70	$ 105
100	.50	2,500	0	250	500	1,250	0	125	250
150	.30	5,000	2,500	0	250	1,500	750	0	75
200	.06	7,500	5,000	2,500	0	450	300	150	0
	1.00					$3,200	$1,085	$ 345	$ 430

                       ↑
                      Optimal Act

$$*EOL(A_j) = \sum_{i=1}^{4} \ell_{ij} P_i$$

Example: $EOL(A_2) = \$250(.14)+0(.50)+2,500(.30)+5,000(.06) = \$1,085.$

Conclusion: Again, the car-rental firm should have 150 cars available.

(d) Revision of prior probability if forecast is fair.

Daily Demand (e_i)	Prior Probability (P_i)	Conditional Probability $P(fair\|e_i)$	Joint Probability $P_i \times P(fair\|e_i)$	Revised Prior Probability $P(e_i\|fair)$
50	.14	.60	.084	.116
100	.50	.75	.375	.517
150	.30	.78	.234	.322
200	.06	.55	.033	.045
	1.00		.726	1.000

(e)   Expected Profit Table Using Revised Probabilities
              If Forecast is For Fair Weather

Daily Demand (e_i)	Revised Probability (P_i)	Expected Profit Alternatives (A_j)			
		50	100	150	200
50	.116	232.00	203.00	174.00	145.00
100	.517	775.50	2,068.00	1,938.75	1,809.50
150	.322	322.00	1,127.00	1,932.00	1,851.50
200	.045	22.50	135.00	247.50	360.00
	1.00	$1,352.00	$3,533.00	$4,292.25	$4,166.00

                                            ↑
                                       Optimal Act

Again, the optimal action is to have 150 cars available daily. However, the forecast of fair weather has increased the difference in the expected profit between having 150 and 200 cars available.

The Analysis of Variance

When dealing with quantitative data, a problem of frequent interest to the researcher is the comparison of several groups. For example, an auditor for the Internal Revenue Service might want to compare the processing speed at several regional offices. In this chapter, then, we are concerned with methods for testing for possible differences between the means of several groups. The methodology considered is classified under the general title of the "analysis of variance." One-factor, randomized block, and two-factor models are described.

MULTIPLE CHOICE

1. The analysis of variance procedures are <u>primarily</u> used to test the hypothesis

   (a) H_0: $p_1 = p_2 = \ldots = p_c$.   (c) H_1: $\sigma_1 = \sigma_2$.

   (b) H_0: $\mu_1 = \mu_2 = \ldots = \mu_c$.   (d) H_1: The data are not a good fit.

2. Which of the following is <u>not</u> an assumption of the analysis of variance?

   (a) normality
   (b) equality of variance from group to group
   (c) qualitative data
   (d) independence of observations.

3. The between groups variation measures

   (a) the difference between each observation (X_{ij}) and the grand mean ($\overline{\overline{X}}$).

(b) the difference between each sample mean $(\overline{X}_j)$ and the grand mean $(\overline{\overline{X}})$.

(c) the difference between each observation (X_{ij}) and its own sample mean $(\overline{X}_j)$.

(d) the difference between each sample mean $(\overline{X}_j)$ and each standard deviation (S_j).

4. If the computed F statistic is less than the critical F value we may

(a) reject H_0 since there is evidence that all the means are different.
(b) reject H_0 since there is evidence that at least one pair of means are different.
(c) not reject H_0 because ther is a mistake in the computations.
(d) not reject H_0 since there is no evidence that the means are different.

5. Given the following information: n = 25, c = 5, SSB = 80.0, SST = 180.0

(a) at the .01 level the critical F value is $F_{.01,4,25} = 4.18$.
(b) at the .01 level the critical F value is $F_{.01,5,20} = 4.10$.
(c) at the .01 level the critical F value is $F_{.01,4,20} = 4.43$.
(d) at the .01 level the critical F value cannot be determined from this data.

6. The Hartley test is used

(a) to test for the differences in the means.
(b) to test for the differences in the proportions.
(c) to test for the differences in the variances.
(d) to test for the differences in statistical power.

EXAMPLES

I. A consumer research organization is interested in the amount of mileage per gallon of gasoline achieved by 4 different brands of compact automobiles under similar driving conditions. A random sample of 6 automobiles is selected from each of the 4 brands of compact automobiles considered (i.e., W.X,Y,Z).

A. At the .01 level of significance, is there evidence of a difference in the variances of the 4 brands of automobiles?

B. At the .01 level of significance, is there evidence of a difference in the average mileage per gallon of gasoline achieved by the 4 brands of automobiles?

C. At the .01 level of significance, determine which of the 4 brands of automobiles are significantly different from each other.

SOLUTION

A. H_0: $\sigma_W^2 = \sigma_X^2 = \sigma_Y^2 = \sigma_Z^2$

H_1: Not all σ_j^2 are equal (j = W,X,Y,Z)

$\alpha = .01$.

Decision rule:

Reject H_o if $F_{MAX(4,5)} > 28$.

Otherwise, do not reject H_o.

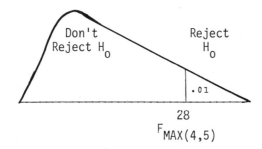

Don't Reject H_o

Reject H_o

.01

28

$F_{MAX(4,5)}$

The following table gives the number of miles per gallon of gasoline achieved by the automobiles under similar conditions:

W	X	Y	Z
32	29	34	29
30	27	31	24
34	32	35	28
31	28	38	28
37	33	35	30
40	31	37	23

T_j 　204　180　210　162　　$GT = \sum\limits_{j=1}^{4} T_j = 756$

n_j 　6　6　6　6

$\overline{X}_j$ 　34　30　35　27　　$n = \sum\limits_{j=1}^{4} n_j = 24$

T_j^2 　41,616　32,400　44,100　26,244　　$(GT)^2 = 571,536$

$\dfrac{T_j^2}{n_j}$ 　6,936　5,400　7,350　4,374　　$\dfrac{(GT)^2}{n} = \dfrac{571,536}{24} = 23,814$

$\sum\limits_{i=1}^{n_j} X_{ij}^2$ 　7,010　5,428　7,380　4,414　　$\sum\limits_{j=1}^{4} \dfrac{T_j^2}{n_j} = 24,060$

S_j^2 　14,8　5.6　6.0　8.0　　$\sum\limits_{j=1}^{4} \sum\limits_{i=1}^{n_j} X_{ij}^2 = 24,232$

Test statistic:

$$F_{MAX(c,(\overline{n} - 1))} = \frac{S^2_{MAX}}{S^2_{MIN}}$$

134

where

c = number of groups = 4

$$\bar{n} = \frac{\sum\limits_{j=1}^{c} n_j}{c} = \frac{n}{c} = \frac{24}{4} = 6 \text{ (only integer portion of value is used)}$$

S_{MAX}^2 = largest sample variance = S_W^2 = 14.8

S_{MIN}^2 = smallest sample variance = S_X^2 = 5.6.

$$F_{MAX(4,5)} = \frac{14.8}{5.6} = 2.64.$$

Conclusion: Since $F_{MAX(4,5)}$ = 2.64 is less than the critical value (28), we do not reject H_0. There is no evidence of a difference in the variances of the 4 brands of automobiles.

B. H_0: $\mu_W = \mu_X = \mu_Y = \mu_Z$ (i.e., There are no differences in the mean amount of mileage per gallon of gasoline achieved by the 4 brands of automobiles.)

H_1: There is a difference in the mean amount of mileage per gallon of gasoline achieved by at least one pair of automobiles.

α = .01.

Decision Rule:

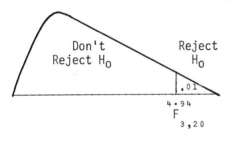

Reject H_0 if $F_{3,20}$ > 4.94.
Otherwise, do not reject H_0.

Don't Reject H_0

Reject H_0

.01

4.94

$F_{3,20}$

Sample results and test statistic:

$$SSB = \sum_{j=1}^{4} \frac{T_j^2}{n_j} - \frac{(GT)^2}{n} = 24{,}060 - 23{,}814 = 246.$$

$$SSW = \sum_{j=1}^{4} \sum_{i=1}^{n_j} X_{ij}^2 - \sum_{j=1}^{4} \frac{T_j^2}{n_j} = 24{,}232 - 24{,}060 = 172.$$

$$SST = \sum_{j=1}^{4} \sum_{i=1}^{n_j} X_{ij}^2 - \frac{(GT)^2}{n} = 24{,}232 - 23{,}814 = 418.$$

135

Analysis of Variance Table

Source	Sums of Squares	Degrees of Freedom	Variances	F
Between Brands	246	$c - 1 =$ $4 - 1 = 3$	$S_B^2 = \dfrac{246}{3} = 82$	
Within Brands	172	$n - c =$ $24 - 4 = 20$	$S_W^2 = \dfrac{172}{20} = 8.6$	$F_{calc} = \dfrac{82}{8.6} = 9.53$
Total	418	$n - 1 =$ $24 - 1 = 23$		

Conclusion: Reject H_0 since 9.53 > 4.94. There is a significant difference between at least one pair of the automobiles in terms of the mean amount of mileage per gallon of gasoline achieved.

C. Please remember that the Tukey T method is appropriate to use only when significant differences in the means of the groups are found. First, we compute absolute differences $|\bar{x}_j - \bar{x}_{j'}|$ among are $c(c-1)/2$ pairs of means. Since there are c=4 groups, there are $4(4-1)/2=6$ possible pairwise comparisons to be made:

1. $|\bar{X}_W - \bar{X}_X| = |34 - 30| = 4$

2. $|\bar{X}_W - \bar{X}_y| = |34 - 35| = 1$

3. $|\bar{X}_W - \bar{X}_z| = |34 - 27| = 7$

4. $|\bar{X}_X - \bar{X}_y| = |30 - 35| = 5$

5. $|\bar{X}_X - \bar{X}_z| = |30 - 27| = 3$

6. $|\bar{X}_y - \bar{X}_z| = |35 - 27| = 8$

Second, we calculate the critical range:

$$\text{critical range} = Q_{\alpha,\ c,\ n-c} \sqrt{\dfrac{S_W^2}{n_j}}$$

$$= Q_{.01,4,20} \sqrt{\dfrac{8.6}{6}}$$

$$= (5.02)(1.197)$$

$$= 6.01$$

Third, we compare the absolute differences to the critical value.

Since 7 > 6.01 and 8 > 6.01, we would conclude that there is a significant difference between brand W and brand Z and there is a significant
difference between brand Y and brand Z. All other differences are
deemed "due to chance."

II. Suppose that a discount store chain has three branches in the metropolitan area. We would like to rate the clothing carried at these branch
stores. Each branch is to be evaluated once by each of six different
fashion designers (raters), differing with respect to their years of
experience. These ratings represent averages with respect to the trendi-
ness, display, sizes and selection of the clothing. The results are
summarized below:

Fashion Designer	Branch Uptown	Midtown	Downtown	Sums
1	25.4	24.5	24.2	74.1
2	25.4	23.7	24.7	73.8
3	25.8	24.4	26.0	76.2
4	24.4	23.3	24.3	72.0
5	24.2	23.6	23.9	71.7
6	26.0	23.9	25.1	75.0
Sums	151.2	143.4	148.2	442.8

Test the hypothesis that population mean ratings are the same in all
branch locations (use $\alpha = .01$).

SOLUTION

Use the randomized block design.
We obtain the following information directly from the table:

$r=6$, $c=3$, $\overline{X}_1. = \frac{74.1}{3} = 24.7$; $\overline{X}_2. = \frac{73.8}{3} = 24.6$;

$\overline{X}_3. = \frac{76.2}{3} = 25.4$; $\overline{X}_4. = \frac{72.0}{3} = 24.0$; $\overline{X}_5. = \frac{71.7}{3} = 23.9$;

$\overline{X}_6. = \frac{75.0}{3} = 25.0$; $\overline{X}_{.1} = \frac{151.2}{6} = 25.2$; $\overline{X}_{.2} = \frac{143.4}{6} = 23.9$

$\overline{X}_{.3} = \frac{148.2}{6} = 24.7$, GT = 442.8

$\sum_{j=1}^{c} \sum_{i=1}^{r} X_{ij}^2 = 25.4^2 + 24.5^2 + \ldots + 25.1^2 = 10904.76$

$\sum_{i=1}^{r} \frac{X_{i.}^2}{c} = \frac{74.1^2 + 73.8^2 + \ldots + 75.0^2}{3} = 10897.86$

137

$$\sum_{j=1}^{c} \frac{X_{\cdot j}^2}{r} = \frac{151.2^2 + 143.4^2 + 148.2^2}{6} = 10898.04$$

$$\frac{(GT)^2}{rc} = \frac{442.8^2}{6(3)} = 10892.88$$

Obtaining the sums of squares:

$$SST = \sum_{j=1}^{c} \sum_{i=1}^{r} X_{ij}^2 - \frac{(GT)^2}{rc}$$

$$= 10904.76 - 10892.88 = 11.88$$

$$SSTR = \sum_{j=1}^{c} \frac{X_{\cdot j}^2}{r} - \frac{(GT)^2}{rc}$$

$$= 10898.04 - 10892.88 = 5.16$$

$$SSBL = \sum_{i=1}^{r} \frac{X_{i \cdot}^2}{c} - \frac{(GT)^2}{rc}$$

$$= 10897.86 - 10892.88 = 4.98$$

$$SSE = \sum_{j=1}^{c} \sum_{i=1}^{r} X_{ij}^2 - \sum_{j=1}^{c} \frac{X_{\cdot j}^2}{r} - \sum_{i=1}^{r} \frac{X_{i \cdot}^2}{c} + \frac{(GT)^2}{rc}$$

$$= 10904.76 - 10898.04 - 10897.86 + 10892.88$$

$$= 1.74$$

Obtaining the mean squares (i.e., variances):

$$S_{TR}^2 = \frac{SSTR}{c-1} = \frac{5.16}{2} = 2.580$$

$$S_{BL}^2 = \frac{SSBL}{r-1} = \frac{4.98}{5} = .996$$

$$S_E^2 = \frac{SSE}{(r-1)(c-1)} = \frac{1.74}{10} = .174$$

To test the null hypothesis that population mean ratings are the same in all branch locations, we calculate the following:

$$H_0: \mu_U = \mu_M = \mu_D$$
$$H_1: \text{Not all } \mu_j \text{ are equal}$$

$$F = \frac{S^2_{TR}}{S^2_E} = \frac{2.58}{.174} = 14.83$$

Using $\alpha = .01$, we compare this to our critical value

$$F_{(c-1), (c-1)(r-1)} = F_{(2,10)} = 7.56$$

There is evidence, at the .01 level of significance, to reject the null hypothesis. We may conclude that there are differences among the branch locations with respect to the clothing they carry.

This entire problem may be summarized in an analysis of variance table:

Analysis of Variance Table for the Randomized Block Design

Source	Sums of Squares	Degrees of Freedom	Variance	F
Among Branch Locations	5.16	2	3.580	14.83
Among Fashing Designers	4.98	5	0.996	5.72
Error	1.74	10	0.174	
Total	11.88	17		

III. An absent-minded professor has been known to continue lecturing after the end of the class period. Some of his students decide to keep track of this "habit." They randomly sample his day and evening Statistics, Advanced Statistics and FORTRAN classes to note the time (nearest minute) that his lecture extends beyond the class. The data are presented below:

Data for a Two-way Analysis of Variance (Minutes as Dependent Variable)

		Course			
		Statistics	Adv.Statistics	FORTRAN	Totals
Session	Day	0,4,8	6,8,10	4,6,8	54
	Evening	6,10,14	0,2,4	9,12,15	72
	Totals	42	30	54	126

These students would like to know whether the session and/or particular course predict the "extra" class time. Conduct the analysis at the .05 level of significance.

SOLUTION

Let A = session
    B = course

If we refer to the above table we have:

r = 2   c = 3   n = 3

$X_{1..} = 54$ $X_{2..} = 72$

$X_{.1.} = 42$ $X_{.2.} = 30$ $X_{.3.} = 54$

$X_{11.} = 12$ $X_{12.} = 24$ $X_{13.} = 18$

$X_{21.} = 30$ $X_{22.} = 6$ $X_{23.} = 36$

GT = 126

$$\sum_{i=1}^{r} \sum_{j=1}^{c} \sum_{k=1}^{n} X_{ijk}^2 = 0^2 + 4^2 + 8^2 + \ldots + 15^2 = 1198$$

$$\sum_{i=1}^{r} \frac{X_{i..}^2}{cn} = \frac{54^2 + 72^2}{3(3)} = 900$$

$$\sum_{j=1}^{c} \frac{X_{.j.}^2}{rn} = \frac{42^2 + 30^2 + 54^2}{2(3)} = 930$$

$$\sum_{i=1}^{r} \sum_{j=1}^{c} \frac{X_{ij.}^2}{n} = \frac{12^2 + 24^2 + \ldots + 36^2}{3} = 1092$$

$$\frac{(GT)^2}{rcn} = \frac{126^2}{2(3)(3)} = 882$$

Obtaining the sums of squares:

$$SST = \sum_{i=1}^{r} \sum_{j=1}^{c} \sum_{k=1}^{n} X_{ijk}^2 - \frac{(GT)^2}{rcn} = 1198 - 882 = 316$$

$$SSFA = \sum_{i=1}^{r} \frac{X_{i..}^2}{cn} - \frac{(GT)^2}{rcn} = 900 - 882 = 18$$

$$SSFB = \sum_{j=1}^{c} \frac{X_{.j.}^2}{rn} - \frac{(GT)^2}{rcn} = 930 - 882 = 48$$

$$SSAB = \sum_{i=1}^{r} \sum_{j=1}^{c} \frac{X_{ij.}^2}{n} - \sum_{i=1}^{r} \frac{X_{i..}^2}{cn} - \sum_{j=1}^{c} \frac{X_{.j.}^2}{rn} + \frac{(GT)^2}{rcn}$$

140

$$= 1092 - 900 - 930 + 882 = 144$$

$$SSE = \sum_{i=1}^{r} \sum_{j=1}^{c} \sum_{k=1}^{n} X_{ijk}^2 - \sum_{i=1}^{r} \sum_{j=1}^{c} \frac{X_{ij.}^2}{n} = 1198 - 1092 = 106$$

Obtaining the mean squares (i.e., variances):

$$S_A^2 = \frac{SSFA}{r-1} = \frac{18}{1} = 18$$

$$S_B^2 = \frac{SSFB}{c-1} = \frac{48}{2} = 24$$

$$S_{AB}^2 = \frac{SSAB}{(r-1)(c-1)} = \frac{144}{2} = 72$$

$$S_E^2 = \frac{SSE}{rc(n-1)} = \frac{106}{6(2)} = 8.83$$

Let us now present this information in an Analysis of Variance Summary Table:

Analysis of Variance Summary Table

Source	Sums of Squares	Degrees of Freedom	Variance	F
Session	18	1	18	2.04
Course	48	2	24	2.72
Session*course	144	2	72	8.15
Error	106	12	8.83	
Total	316	17		

At the .05 level, the critical value for the test on the session is $F_{(1,12)} = 4.75$. Therefore, we do not reject H_o and conclude that there is no significant difference between the day and evening sessions in the amount of "overtime" lecturing, i.e., 2.04 < 4.75.

At the .05 level, the critical value for the test on the course is $F_{(2,12)} = 3.89$. Therefore, we do not reject H_o and conclude that there is no significant difference among the various courses in the amount of "extra" lecturing, i.e., 2.72 < 3.89.

At the .05 level, the critical value for the test on the session and course interaction is $F_{(2,12)} = 8.15$. We reject H_o, concluding that

141

a significant interaction effect between the session and course is present, i.e., 8.15 > 3.89. Therefore, the differences in mean "extra lecture time" among various types of courses is not constant over day versus evening sessions.

REVIEW PROBLEM

A radio station is interested in the listening habits of its audience. It takes a random sample of 25 of its listeners. They are divided into the following age groups and the amount of time spent listening to the news in hours per week is recorded:

18-24	25-35	35-54	Over 54
1	4	5	6
1	6	7	7
0	2	4	5
2	3	3	4
	3	3	5
	2	4	3
	3	2	
	5		
—	—	—	—

A. At the .05 level of significance, is there evidence of a difference in the variance of the amount of time spent listening to the news between the various age groups?

B. At the .05 level of significance, is there evidence of a difference in the average amount of time spent listening to the news between the various age groups?

142

SOLUTION TO REVIEW PROBLEM

A. H_0: $\sigma^2_{18-24} = \sigma^2_{25-34} = \sigma^2_{35-54} = \sigma^2_{54+}$

H_1: Not all σ_j^2 are equal.

$\alpha = .05$.

Decision rule: Reject H_0 if $F_{MAX(4,5)} > 13.7$. Otherwise, don't reject H_0.

	Age Groups				
	18-24	25-34	35-54	Over 54	
T_j	4	28	28	30	$GT = \sum\limits_{j=1}^{4} T_j = 90$
n_j	4	8	7	6	$n = \sum\limits_{j=1}^{4} n_j = 25$
$\overline{X}_j$	1	3.5	4	5	$\dfrac{(GT)^2}{n} = \dfrac{(90)^2}{25} = 324$
T_j^2	16	784	784	900	$\sum\limits_{j=1}^{4} \dfrac{T_j^2}{n_j} = 364$
$\dfrac{T_j^2}{n_j}$	4	98	112	150	$\sum\limits_{j=1}^{4} \sum\limits_{i=1}^{n_j} X_{ij}^2 = 406$
$\sum\limits_{i=1}^{n_j} X_{ij}^2$	6	112	128	160	
S_j^2	.67	2	2.67	2	

Test statistic:

$$F_{MAX(4,5)} = \frac{S^2_{35-54}}{S^2_{18-24}} = \frac{2.67}{.67} = 3.99.$$

Conclusion: Since $F_{MAX(4,5)} = 3.99$ is less than the critical value (13.7), do not reject H_0. There appears to be no evidence that the variances of the amount of time spent listening to the news is different between the various age groups.

B. $H_0: \mu_{18-24} = \mu_{25-34} = \mu_{35-54} = \mu_{54+}$

H_1: Not all the means are equal.

$\alpha = .05$.

Decision rule: Reject H_0 if $F_{3,21} > 3.07$. Otherwise, do not reject H_0.

Sample results and test statistics:

$$SSB = \sum_{j=1}^{4} \frac{T_j^2}{n_j} - \frac{(GT)^2}{n} = 364 - 324 = 40.$$

$$SSW = \sum_{j=1}^{4} \sum_{i=1}^{n_j} X_{ij}^2 - \sum_{j=1}^{4} \frac{T_j^2}{n_j} = 406 - 364 = 42.$$

$$SST = \sum_{j=1}^{4} \sum_{i=1}^{n_j} X_{ij}^2 - \frac{(GT)^2}{n} = 406 - 324 = 82.$$

Analysis of Variance Table

Source	Sums of Squares	Degrees of Freedom	Variances	F
Between Age Groups	40	$c - 1 =$ $4 - 1 = 3$	$S_B^2 = \frac{40}{3} = 13.33$	$F_{calc} = \frac{13.33}{2.00} = 6.67$
Within Age Groups	42	$n - c =$ $25 - 4 = 21$	$S_W^2 = \frac{42}{21} = 2.00$	
Total	82	$n - 1 =$ $25 - 1 = 24$		

Conclusion: Reject H_0 since 6.67 > 3.07. There is a significant difference in the average amount of time spent listening to the news between at least two of the age groups at the .05 level of significance.

144

15 Nonparametric Methods

In Chapters 10-12 and 14 the so-called "classical methods" of hypothesis testing were described. Nevertheless, a problem of frequent concern to the researcher in the social sciences and in business is what kinds of testing procedures to choose from if (a) it is deemed inappropriate to make the more rigorous assumptions of the aforementioned classical methods; (b) the measurements attained on the data are only qualitative or in ranks; or (c) it is desired to treat such problems as randomness, trend, cyclical effects, symmetry or goodness of fit rather than testing hypotheses about particular population parameters. Hence, for such situations as these, a set of nonparametric procedures were devised. This chapter, then, focuses on the development of nonparametric methods of hypothesis testing. In particular, seven useful procedures are discussed: (1) the Wald-Wolfowitz one-sample runs test for randomness; (2) the Wilcoxon one-sample signed-ranks test; (3) the Wilcoxon paired-sample signed-ranks test; (4) the Wilcoxon rank sum test; (5) the Kruskal-Wallis test for C independent samples; (6) the Friedman rank test; and (7) Spearman's rank correlation procedure. In addition, numerous concepts such as levels of measurement, robustness, randomness, runs, trend, signs and power are discussed.

MULTIPLE CHOICE

1. The classification of various business firms into particular industrial groups is an example of

   (a) a ratio scale.
   (b) an interval scale.
   (c) an ordinal scale.
   (d) a nominal scale.

2. A consecutive series of similar items in a test for randomness is known
   (a) as a sign.   (c) as an absolute normal score.
   (b) as a robust procedure.   (d) as a run.

3. In performing the Wilcoxon one-sample signed-ranks test, absolute difference scores of zero
   (a) are discarded.   (c) are given the rank -1.
   (b) are given the rank +1.   (d) do not occur in practice.

4. The sum of the first n consecutive ranks (integers) is
   (a) $n(n + 1)/4$ (c) $n(n + 1)/2$

   (b) $\sqrt{\dfrac{n(n + 1)(2n + 1)}{24}}$ (d) None of the above.

5. The Wilcoxon paired-sample signed-ranks test is a nonparametric analogue of the
   (a) χ^2 test for independence.   (c) analysis of variance F test.
   (b) runs test for randomness.   (d) t test for related samples.

6. As the sample sizes in each of the C groups gets large, the Kruskal-Wallis test statistic H may be approximated by
   (a) Z.   (c) $t_{(C-1)}$.
   (b) $\chi^2_{(C-1)}$.   (d) $F_{(1,C-1)}$

EXAMPLES

I. A typing test was given to a sample of 15 candidates for a secretarial position. The data below represent the number of errors made by each candidate on the test. Using a .05 level of significance, is there evidence to believe that the median number of errors is 10?

    Number of Errors (X_i): 5, 16, 4, 2, 11, 7, 3, 10, 0, 6, 9, 1, 9, 3, 8.

SOLUTION

    We use the Wilcoxon one-sample signed-ranks test.

    H_0: Median = 10 errors.

    H_1: Median $\neq$ 10 errors.

    α = .05.

    Decision rule: Since n $\leq$ 20 use the table of lower and upper critical values W of Wilcoxon signed-ranks test to obtain critical values for the test statistic W. Reject H_0 if W $\leq$ 21 or if W $\geq$ 84. Otherwise, do not reject H_0.

    Sample result and test statistic:

X_i	$d_i = X_i - 10$	$|d_i|$	R_i	Sign of d_i
5	-5	5	7	-
16	6	6	8.5	+
4	-6	6	8.5	-
2	-8	8	12	-
11	1	1	2	+
7	-3	3	5	-
3	-7	7	10.5	-
10	0	-	-	Discard
0	-10	10	14	-
6	-4	4	6	-
9	-1	1	2	-
1	-9	9	13	-
9	-1	1	2	-
3	-7	7	10.5	-
8	-2	2	4	-

$$W = \sum_{i=1}^{14} R_i^+ = 8.5 + 2 = 10.5.$$

Conclusion: Since $W = 10.5$ is less than the critical value (21), we reject H_0 at the .05 level of significance. The median number of errors appears to be lower than 10.

II. Random samples of 14 Brand X transistors and 12 Brand Y transistors were obtained for experimental purposes. Recorded below are the lifetimes of these transistors (in hundreds of hours):

X: 42, 44, 45, 47, 52, 53, 57, 68, 69, 72, 79, 81, 88, 94.

Y: 51, 60, 64, 75, 80, 86, 97, 100, 120, 128, 136, 137.

At the .01 level of significance, is there any significant difference in the durability of Brand X and Brand Y transistors?

SOLUTION

We use the Wilcoxon rank sum test for the difference between two mutually independent sample groups drawn from the same population or identical populations.

H_0: $M_1 = M_2$ (The median lifetimes are equal.)

H_1: $M_1 \neq M_2$ (The median lifetimes are not equal.)

$\alpha = .01$.

Decision rule: Since n_1 and n_2 are > 10, the test statistic T_{n_1} is approximately normally distributed.

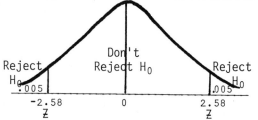

Reject H_0 .005   -2.58   Z

Don't Reject H_0 0

Reject H_0 .005   2.58   Z

Therefore, reject H_0 if $Z > 2.58$ or if $Z < -2.58$. Otherwise, don't reject H_0.

Sample results:

Lifetimes of Transistors (100 hours)		Combined Rankings of Lifetimes of Transistors from X and Y	
X	Y	X	Y
42	51	1	5
44	60	2	9
45	64	3	10
47	75	4	14
52	80	6	16
53	86	7	18
57	97	8	21
68	100	11	22
69	120	12	23
72	128	13	24
79	136	15	25
81	137	17	26
88		19	
94		20	
$n_2 = 14$	$n_1 = 12$	$T_{n_2} = 138$	$T_{n_1} = 213$

Test statistic: $Z \approx \dfrac{T_{n_1} - \mu_{T_{n_1}}}{\sigma_{T_{n_1}}}$

where T_{n_1} = the summation of the ranks assigned to the n_1 observations in the smaller sample = 213.

$\mu_{T_{n_1}}$ = the mean value of T_{n_1} = $n_1(n+1)/2 = 12(27)/2 = 162$.

$$\sigma_{T_{n_1}} = \text{the standard deviation of } T_{n_1} = \sqrt{\frac{n_1 n_2 (n+1)}{12}} = \sqrt{\frac{12(14)(27)}{12}}$$

$$= \sqrt{378} = 19.4422.$$

Thus, $Z \approx \dfrac{213 - 162}{19.4422} = \dfrac{51}{19.4422} = 2.62.$

Conclusion: Since $Z = 2.62$ exceeds the critical value (2.58), we reject H_0. There is evidence of a significant difference between the lifetimes of transistors of the two brands (X and Y) at the .01 level of significance.

III. It is believed that the pulse rate is increased after exercise. The pulse rates of a sample of 8 male students before and after exercise are presented below:

Student	Before	After
I	62	70
II	69	67
III	71	86
IV	58	77
V	75	75
VI	68	81
VII	60	80
VIII	72	82

At the .01 level of significance, is there evidence to conclude that the pulse rate is increased after exercise?

SOLUTION

We use the Wilcoxon paired-sample signed-ranks test.

H_0: $M_d \leq 0$ (Median pulse rate does not increase after exercise.)

H_1: $M_d > 0$ (Median pulse rate increases after exercise.)

$\alpha = .01.$

Decision rule: Since n $\leq$ 20 use the table of lower and upper critical values W of Wilcoxon signed-ranks test to obtain critical values for the test statistic W. Reject H_0 if W $\geq$ 28. Otherwise, do not reject H_0.

Sample results:

Student	Before	After	d_i = After - Before	$\|d_i\|$	R_i	Sign of d_i
I	62	70	8	8	2	+
II	69	67	-2	2	1	-
III	71	86	15	15	5	+
IV	58	77	19	19	6	+
V	75	75	0	--	-	Discard
VI	68	81	13	13	4	+
VII	60	80	20	20	7	+
VIII	72	82	10	10	3	+

Test Statistic:

$$W = \sum_{i=1}^{n} R_i^+$$

where

n = number of pairs minus any pairs whose D_i is zero = 7

$$\sum_{i=1}^{n} R_i^+ = \text{sum of the positive ranks.}$$

Thus, $W = \sum_{i=1}^{7} R_i^+ = 2 + 5 + 6 + 4 + 7 + 3 = 27.$

Conclusion: Since W = 27 is less than the critical value (28), we do not reject H_0 at the .01 level of significance. There is no evidence that exercise increases pulse rates.

IV   An efficiency expert is hired to evaluate the various training programs
      used to instruct employees on how to assemble printed circuit boards for
      a minicomputer. Eighteen employees are chosen at random and assigned in
      groups of six to each of the three training programs currently being
      used. At the .05 level of significance, do the different training pro-
      grams have an effect on the average number of printed circuit boards
      assembled?

      The number of boards assembled by the employees after a week of training
      are as follows:

Training Programs

I	II	III
42	36	49
41	34	41
39	33	38
41	32	45
37	40	37
40	35	42

SOLUTION

We use the Kruskal-Wallis test for 3 independent samples.

H_0: $M_I = M_{II} = M_{III}$ (The median number of boards assembled by the em-
                                    ployees under the three programs are equal.)

H_1: Not all the medians are equal.

α = .05.

Decision rule:

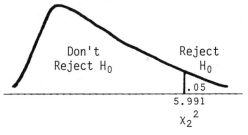

Don't
Reject H_0
Reject
H_0
.05
5.991
X_2^2

Since all n_j's > 5, the test statistic H may be approximated by the x^2
distribution with C-1(or 3-1=2) degrees of freedom. Thus, reject H_0
if H > 5.991. Otherwise don't reject
H_0.

Sample results:

Number of Boards Assembled			Conversion of Number of Boards Assembled to Ranks		
I	II	III	I	II	III
42	36	49	15.5	5	18
41	34	41	13	3	13
39	33	38	9	2	8
41	32	45	13	.1	17
37	40	37	6.5	10.5	6.5
40	35	42	10.5	4	15.5
			T_{n_1} =67.5	T_{n_2} =25.5	T_{n_3} =78

Test statistic:

$$H = \left[\frac{12}{n(n+1)} \left(\sum_{j=1}^{C} \frac{T_{n_j}^2}{n_j} \right) \right] - 3(n+1) = \left[\frac{12}{18(18+1)} \left(\sum_{i=1}^{3} \frac{T_{n_j}^2}{n_j} \right) \right] - 3(18+1)$$

$$= \left[\frac{12}{342} \left(\frac{(67.5)^2}{6} + \frac{(25.5)^2}{6} + \frac{(78)^2}{6} \right) \right] - 3(19)$$

$$= \frac{12}{342} (1881.75) - 57 = 66.026 - 57 = 9.026.$$

Conclusion: Since the computed value of the test statistic H (9.026) exceeds the critical value ($\chi_2^2 = 5.991$) we reject H_0 at the .05 level of significance. The efficiency expert may conclude that at least two of the training programs are different with respect to the number of printed circuit boards assembled.

V. You and eight of your friends conduct a "pizza-eating" experiment so that four kinds of pizza are rated by nine pizza "gourmets." A rating on a 5-point scale (1 - very bad, 5 = very good) is given for each of the following characteristics: crust, cheese, sauce and spices. The table below displays the summated ratings accumulated over all four characteristics.

Summated Ratings of Four Kinds of Pizza

Gourmet	Kind of Pizza			
	Ray's	Steve's	Rio's	Albanese's
1	15	18	20	20
2	16	15	17	18
3	17	17	18	19
4	20	10	20	12
5	11	14	13	18
6	15	15	12	17
7	18	20	19	17
8	16	13	12	15
9	14	11	15	16

(a) Convert the data to ranks

(b) Test the null hypothesis that the median summated rating scores for the four kinds of pizza are equal. (Remember: Your alternative hypothesis will test if at least two of the kinds of pizza have median summated rating scores which differ).

Use the α = .05 level of significance.

SOLUTION

(a)

Converting the Data to Ranks

Gourmet	Kind of Pizza			
	Ray's	Steve's	Rio's	Albanese's
1	1.0	2.0	3.5	3.5
2	2.0	1.0	3.0	4.0
3	1.5	1.5	3.0	4.0
4	3.5	1.0	3.5	2.0
5	1.0	3.0	2.0	4.0
6	2.5	2.5	1.0	4.0
7	2.0	4.0	3.0	1.0
8	4.0	2.0	1.0	3.0
9	2.0	1.0	3.0	4.0
Rank Totals	19.5	18.0	23.0	29.5

(b) H_0: $M_{RAY} = M_{STV} = M_{RIO} = M_{ALB}$ (There is no difference in the quality of the four pizzas)

H_1: Not all M_j's are equal (where j = Ray's, Steve's, Rio's, Albanese's)

We check the rankings:

$$R._1 + R._2 + R._3 + R._4 = \frac{n\,c\,(c+1)}{2}$$

From the above data:

$$19.5 + 18.0 + 23.0 + 29.5 = \frac{9(4)(5)}{2}$$
$$90 = 90$$

Using the Friedman rank test statistic:

$$F_R = \frac{12}{n\,c\,(c+1)} \sum_{j=1}^{c} R._j^2 - 3n\,(c+1)$$

$$= \frac{12}{9(4)(5)} [19.5^2 + 18.0^2 + 23.0^2 + 29.5^2] - 3(9)(5)$$

$$= \frac{12}{180}\; 2103.5 - 135$$

$$= 140.12 - 135$$

$$= 5.233$$

Since the computed F_R statistic does not exceed the critical value ($X_3^2 = 7.815$), we do not reject the null hypothesis at the .05 level of significance. There is no evidence, with respect to the pizzas, of a difference in their quality.

VI. The media director of a large television station was interested in determining whether there was a relationship between sales (in thousands of dollars) and the number of Tv commercials broadcast between 3pm and midnight in a sample of 9 test cities. The data are listed below:

City	1	2	3	4	5	6	7	8	9
Tv Commercials (X)	11	13	7	12	10	9	14	16	8
Sales (Y)	8	14	5	7	10	15	13	11	9

Measure the rank correlation between sales and the number of Tv commercials broadcast. Is there evidence of a relationship at the .01 level of significance?

SOLUTION

We use Spearman rank correlation (denoted r_s).

H_0: There is no relationship between sales and the number of Tv commercials broadcast.

H_1: There is a relationship between sales and the number of Tv commercials broadcast.

$\alpha = .01$.

Decision rule:

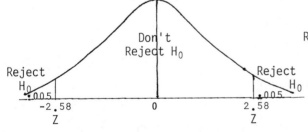

Reject H_0 if $Z < -2.58$ or if $Z > 2.58$. Otherwise, do not reject H_0.

Sample results:

City	Tv Commercials (X)	Sales (Y)	Rank R_X	R_Y	d_R $(R_X - R_Y)$	d_R^2
1	11	8	5	3	2	4
2	13	14	7	8	-1	1
3	7	5	1	1	0	0
4	12	7	6	2	4	16
5	10	10	4	5	-1	1
6	9	15	3	9	-6	36
7	14	13	8	7	1	1
8	16	11	9	6	3	9
9	8	9	2	4	-2	4
					$\Sigma d_{R_i}^2 = 72$	

Test statistic:

$$Z \approx r_s \sqrt{n - 1}$$

where

$$r_s = 1 - \frac{6 \sum_{i=1}^{n} d_{R_i}^2}{n(n^2 - 1)} = 1 - \frac{6(72)}{9(9^2 - 1)} = 1 - \frac{432}{9(81 - 1)} = 1 - \frac{432}{720}$$

$$r_s = 1 - .60 = .40.$$

Thus, $Z \approx .40\sqrt{9 - 1} = .40(2.8284) = 1.13.$

Conclusion: Since $Z \approx 1.13$ falls between the critical Z values $(-2.58 \leq Z \leq 2.58)$, we cannot reject the null hypothesis at the .01 level of significance. There is no evidence that there is a relationship between sales and the number of Tv commercials broadcast.

REVIEW PROBLEMS

I. In the test of a gasoline additive, a group of seven carefully engineered
    cars were run at a testing site under rigorously controlled conditions.
    The number of miles obtained on a single gallon of gasoline were, re-
    spectively, 17, 13, 15, 18, 20, 10 and 16. Is there evidence to believe
    that the median number of miles is more than 14 at the .05 level of
    significance?

II. An industrial firm is interested in the resistance to corrosion of two types of pipe coating. The following data represent the amount of corrosion found on the two types of pipe:

Lead Coated Steel Pipe	Bare Steel Pipe
27	41
18	25
12	20
28	27
11	29
15	18
21	31

At the .05 level of significance, do the two types of pipe coatings differ significantly in their resistance to corrosion?

III. For nine consecutive days coffee was prepared by using two different name brands of drip coffeemakers, and the time (to the nearest tenth of a minute) it takes to make coffee on each machine was recorded:

Drip Coffeemaker	Day								
	1	2	3	4	5	6	7	8	9
I	8.9	8.7	8.8	5.8	6.3	11.0	7.8	10.0	9.1
II	13.3	10.5	12.5	7.2	9.1	9.1	7.8	10.9	10.2

At the .01 level of significance, is there a difference in preparation time between the two name brands of drip coffeemakers?

IV. An experimenter wishes to test whether or not three speed reading teaching methods have identical effects upon reading speed. The following results were collected:

Speed Reading Teaching Methods

I	II	III
425	470	398
391	475	440
443	709	452
412	578	488
377	495	460
395	510	428
406		

At the .01 level of significance, is there a difference between the three speed reading teaching methods with respect to reading speed?

V. The U.S. Armed Services wants to determine if there is a relationship between unemployment rates and recruitment rates. It takes a random sample of twelve recruiting districts and collects the following data:

Recruiting District	Unemployment Rate (X) (No. per 100)	Recruitment Rate (Y) (No. per 10,000)
1	5	83
2	5	94
3	6	98
4	11	152
5	14	199
6	7	107
7	8	124
8	12	206
9	10	163
10	4	92
11	9	131
12	5	90

Measure the rank correlation between unemployment rates and recruitment rates. Is there evidence of a significant relationship at the .05 level of significance?

SOLUTIONS TO REVIEW PROBLEMS

I. Use the Wilcoxon one-sample signed-ranks test.

H_0: Median $\leq$ 14 miles per gallon.

H_1: Median > 14 miles per gallon.

α = .05.

Decision rule: Using the table of critical values, reject H_0 if W $\geq$ 25. Otherwise, don't reject H_0.

Sample result and test statistic:

Car	X_i	$d_i = X_i - 14$	$|d_i|$	R_i	Sign of d_i
1	17	3	3	4	+
2	13	-1	1	1.5	-
3	15	1	1	1.5	+
4	18	4	4	5.5	+
5	20	6	6	7	+
6	10	-4	4	5.5	-
7	16	2	2	3	+

$$W = \sum_{i=1}^{7} R_i^+ = 4 + 1.5 + 5.5 + 7 + 3 = 21.$$

Conclusion: Since W = 21 is less than the critical value (25), we don't reject H_0. There is no evidence to conclude that the median is more than 14 miles to a gallon with this gasoline additive at the .05 level of significance.

II. We use the Wilcoxon rank sum test.

H_0: $M_1 = M_2$ (Median resistance to corrosion is equal.)

H_1: $M_1 \neq M_2$ (Median resistance to corrosion is different.)

α = .05.

Decision rule: Since both n_1 and n_2 are $\leq$ 10, lower and upper critical values for the rank sum test statistic T_{n_1} are obtained. Hence, we reject H_0 if $T_{n_1} \leq$ 36 or if $T_{n_1} \geq$ 69. Otherwise, don't reject H_0.

162

Sample result and test statistic:

Corrosion		Conversion of Corrosion to Ranks	
Lead Coated Pipe	Bare Pipe	Lead Coated Pipe	Bare Pipe
27	41	9.5	14
18	25	4.5	8
12	20	2	6
28	27	11	9.5
11	29	1	12
15	18	3	4.5
21	31	7	13
		$T_{n_1} = 38$	$T_{n_2} = 67$

Conclusion: Since the observed value $T_{n_1} = 38$ falls between the critical values 36 and 69, H_0 cannot be rejected at the .05 level of significance. It may be concluded that there is no evidence of any significant differences between the two types of pipe coatings with respect to corrosion resistance.

III. We use the Wilcoxon paired-sample signed-ranks test.

H_0: $M_d = 0$ (There is no difference in the time it takes to make coffee.)

H_1: $M_d \neq 0$ (There is a difference in the time it takes to make coffee.)

$\alpha = .01$.

Decision rule: Reject H_0 if $W \leq 0$ or if $W \geq 36$. Otherwise, do not reject H_0.

Sample results:

Day	Coffeemaker I	Coffeemaker II	$d_i = I - II$	$\|d_i\|$	R_i	Sign of d_i
1	8.9	13.3	-4.4	4.4	8	-
2	8.7	10.5	-1.8	1.8	4	-
3	8.8	12.5	-3.7	3.7	7	-
4	5.8	7.2	-1.4	1.4	3	-
5	6.3	9.1	-2.8	2.8	6	-
6	11.0	9.1	1.9	1.9	5	+
7	7.8	7.8	0	-	-	Discard
8	10.0	10.9	- .9	.9	1	-
9	9.1	10.2	-1.1	1.1	2	-

Test statistic:

$$W = \sum_{i=1}^{n} R_i^{+} = 5.$$

Conclusion: Since W = 5 falls between the critical values (0 < W < 36), we do not reject H_0. There is no evidence of a significant difference between the two drip coffeemakers with respect to the time it takes to make coffee at the .01 level of significance.

IV. We use the Kruskal-Wallis test.

$H_0 : M_1 = M_2 = M_3$

H_1: Not all the medians are equal.

$\alpha = .01$.

Decision rule: Using the χ^2 approximation to the test statistic H, we reject H_0 if H > 9.210. Otherwise, do not reject H_0.

Sample results:

I	II	III	Combined Ranks		
			I	II	III
425	470	398	7	13	4
391	475	440	2	14	9
443	709	452	10	19	11
412	578	488	6	18	15
377	495	460	1	16	12
395	510	428	3	17	8
406			5		
			$T_{n_1}=34$	$T_{n_2}=97$	$T_{n_3}=59$	Rank Sums

Test statistic:

$$H = \left[\frac{12}{n(n+1)} \left(\sum_{j=1}^{C} \frac{T_{n_j}^2}{n_j}\right)\right] - 3(n+1)$$

$$= \left[\frac{12}{19(19+1)}\left(\frac{(34)^2}{7} + \frac{(97)^2}{6} + \frac{(59)^2}{6}\right)\right] - 3(20)$$

$$= \frac{12}{380}(2,313.4762) - 60 = 73.057 - 60 = 13.057.$$

Conclusion: Since the computed value H = 13.057 is greater than the critical value ($x_2^2 = 9.210$), we reject H_0 at the .01 level of significance. The experimenter may conclude that at least two of the speed reading teaching methods do not have identical effects upon reading speed.

V.   Use Spearman rank correlation.

H_0: There is no relationship between unemployment rates and recruitment rates.

H_1: There is a relationship between unemployment rates and recruitment rates.

$\alpha = .05$.

Decision rule: Reject H_0 if $Z < -1.96$ or if $Z > 1.96$. Otherwise, do not reject H_0.

Sample results:

Recruiting District	Unemployment Rate (X)	Recruitment Rate (Y)	Rank R_X	Rank R_Y	d_R	d_R^2
1	5	83	3	1	2	4
2	5	94	3	4	-1	1
3	6	98	5	5	0	0
4	11	152	10	9	1	1
5	14	199	12	11	1	1
6	7	107	6	6	0	0
7	8	124	7	7	0	0
8	12	206	11	12	-1	1
9	10	163	9	10	-1	1
10	4	92	1	3	-2	4
11	9	131	8	8	0	0
12	5	90	3	2	1	1
					$\Sigma d_{R_i}^2 = 14$	

Test statistic:

$$Z \approx r_s \sqrt{n - 1}$$

where

$$r_s = 1 - \frac{6 \Sigma d_{R_i}^2}{n(n^2 - 1)} = 1 - \frac{6(14)}{12(12^2 - 1)} = 1 - .049 = .951.$$

Therefore, $Z \simeq .951\sqrt{12 - 1} = 3.15$.

Conclusion: Since $Z \simeq 3.15$ exceeds the critical value (1.96), we reject the null hypothesis at the .05 level of significance. There is evidence of a relationship between unemployment rates and recruitment rates.

16

The Simple Linear Regression Model and Correlation

In our discussion of various statistical methods, we have been primarily concerned with problems involving only a single variable of interest. In simple linear regression and correlation we will examine the relationship between two quantitative variables. Regression analysis utilizes one variable (the independent) for predicting another variable (the dependent), while correlation measures the strength of the association between the two variables. In regression analysis, the Least Squares method is used to determine the two regression coefficients: b_0, the Y intercept, and b_1, the slope. These regression coefficients can then be utilized to predict the value of the dependent variable. Once this prediction is obtained along with the standard error of the estimate (the measure of variation around the line of regression), statistical inference can be utilized to determine the significance of the relationship and to obtain confidence interval estimates. Moreover, residual analysis and other regression diagnostics can be used to evaluate the appropriateness of the developed regression model.

MULTIPLE CHOICE

1. Assuming a linear relationship between X and Y, if the coefficient of correlation (r) equals -.30

   (a) there is no correlation.
   (b) the slope (b_1) is negative.
   (c) variable X is larger than variable Y.
   (d) the variance of Y is negative.

2. The coefficient of determination (r^2) tells us

   (a) that the coefficient of correlation (r) is larger than one.
   (b) whether r has any significance.

(c) that we should not partition the total variation.
(d) the proportion of total variation that is explained.

3. The standard error of the estimate is a measure of

(a) variation around the arithmetic mean.
(b) relationship between the dependent and independent variables.
(c) variation of the regression coefficients.
(d) variation around the fitted line of regression.

4. The slope (b_1) represents

(a) predicted value of Y when X = 0.
(b) the change in Y per unit change in X.
(c) the predicted value of Y.
(d) variation around the line of regression.

5. Testing for the existence of correlation is equivalent to

(a) testing for the existence of the slope (b_1).
(b) testing for the existence of the Y intercept (b_0).
(c) the confidence interval estimate for predicting Y.
(d) None of the above.

6. In performing a regression analysis involving two quantitative variables, we are assuming

(a) the variances of X and Y are equal.
(b) the variation around the line of regression is the same for each X value.
(c) that X and Y are independent.
(d) All of the above.

7. In the early days of the smoking and cancer issue, it was reported that there was a correlation between the amount of smoking and the likelihood of lung cancer. These data suggest that

(a) smoking causes lung cancer.
(b) if we knew how many people actually died of lung cancer, then we could conclude that smoking causes lung cancer.
(c) if we knew that the actual correlation was .7 or higher, then we could conclude that smoking causes lung cancer.
(d) there is evidence of an association between smoking and lung cancer.

8. The value of r^2 for a particular situation is .49. What is the co-efficient of correlation in this situation?

(a) .49
(b) .7
(c) .07
(d) cannot be determined from the information given; we need to know the "direction" of the relationship between X and Y.

9. If the dependent variable increases as the explanatory variable increases in a regression equation, then the coefficient of correlation would be in the range:

(a) 0 to -1   (c) 0 to -2
(b) 0 to -.5   (d) none of these.

The marketing department of a retail chain outlet wishes to determine if there is a relationship between sales volume for a product and the number of radio commercials broadcast in a sample of ten large cities. The data are given as follows:

City	X Radio Commercials (Broadcasts per Day)	Y Sales Volume (Units per Year)
A	11	8,000
B	7	5,000
C	12	9,000
D	8	4,000
E	10	8,000
F	13	10,000
G	8	5,000
H	10	7,000
I	14	10,000
J	7	4,000

(a) Set up a scatter diagram.

(b) Assuming a linear relationship, use the Least Squares method to compute the regression coefficients (b_0 and b_1).

(c) Interpret the meaning of the intercept (b_0) and the slope (b_1) in this problem.

(d) Predict the yearly sales volume in a city in which 8 commercials are broadcast per day.

(e) Compute the standard error of estimate.

(f) Compute the coefficient of determination (r^2) and interpret its meaning in this problem.

(g) Compute the coefficient of correlation (r).

(h) Compute the adjusted r^2.

(i) At the .01 level of significance, is there a relationship between sales volume and number of radio commercials broadcast?

(j) Set up a 99% confidence interval estimate of the average yearly sales volume for all cities in which 8 commercials are broadcast per day.

(k) Set up a 99% interval estimate of sales volume for an individual city that broadcasts 8 radio commercials per day.

(l) Set up the 99% confidence interval estimate of the true slope.

(m) Discuss why you shouldn't predict yearly sales volume in a city which has fewer than 7 broadcasts per day or more than 14 broadcasts per day.

SOLUTION

Computations for sales volume example.

City	X_i Radio Commercials (Broadcast per day)	Y_i Sales Volume (Units per year)	X_i^2	Y_i^2	$X_i Y_i$
A	11	8,000	121	64,000,000	88,000
B	7	5,000	49	25,000,000	35,000
C	12	9,000	144	81,000,000	108,000
D	8	4,000	64	16,000,000	32,000
E	10	8,000	100	64,000,000	80,000
F	13	10,000	169	100,000,000	130,000
G	8	5,000	64	25,000,000	40,000
H	10	7,000	100	49,000,000	70,000
I	14	10,000	196	100,000,000	140,000
J	7	4,000	49	16,000,000	28,000
	100	70,000	1,056	540,000,000	751,000
	$\sum_{i=1}^{10} X_i$	$\sum_{i=1}^{10} Y_i$	$\sum_{i=1}^{10} X_i^2$	$\sum_{i=1}^{10} Y_i^2$	$\sum_{i=1}^{10} X_i Y_i$
	$\bar{X} = 10$	$\bar{Y} = 7,000$			

171

(a) Scatter diagram of Radio Commercials versus Sales Volume.

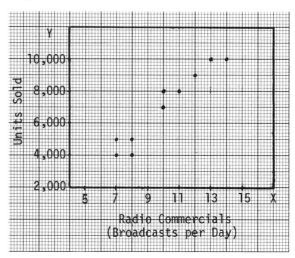

(b) Regression coefficients.

$$b_1 = \frac{n \sum\limits_{i=1}^{n} X_i Y_i - (\sum\limits_{i=1}^{n} X_i)(\sum\limits_{i=1}^{n} Y_i)}{n \sum\limits_{i=1}^{n} X_i^2 - (\sum\limits_{i=1}^{n} X_i)^2} = \frac{10(751,000) - (100)(70,000)}{10(1,056) - (100)^2}$$

$$= \frac{510,000}{560} = 910.714.$$

$$b_0 = \bar{Y} - b_1 \bar{X} = 7,000 - (910.714)(10) = 7,000 - 9,107.14 = -2,107.14.$$

$$\hat{Y}_i = -2,107.14 + 910.714 X_i$$

(c) The slope in this problem is 910.714. This means that for each unit increase in radio commercials, the sales volume will increase by 910.714 units.

(d) Predict yearly sales volume if X_i = 8 commercials.

$$\hat{Y}_i = b_0 + b_1 X_i = -2,107.14 + 910.714(8) = -2,107.14 + 7,285.712$$

$$= 5,178.572.$$ The predicted average sales volume is 5,179 units when 8 radio commercials are broadcast per day.

(e) Standard error of estimate, $S_{YX} = \sqrt{\dfrac{\text{Unexplained Sums of Squares}}{n-2}} =$

$$\sqrt{\frac{\sum\limits_{i=1}^{n} Y_i^2 - b_0 \sum\limits_{i=1}^{n} Y_i - b_1 \sum\limits_{i=1}^{n} X_i Y_i}{n-2}}$$

$$S_{YX} = \sqrt{\frac{540,000,000 - (-2,107.14)(70,000) - (910.714)(751,000)}{10 - 2}}$$

$$= \sqrt{\frac{3,553,586}{8}} = \sqrt{444,198.25} = 666.48 \text{ units.}$$

(f) Coefficient of determination, $r^2 = \dfrac{\text{Explained Sums of Squares}}{\text{Total Sums of Squares}}$

$$r^2 = \frac{b_0 \sum\limits_{i=1}^{n} Y_i + b_1 \sum\limits_{i=1}^{n} X_i Y_i - \dfrac{\left(\sum\limits_{i=1}^{n} Y_i\right)^2}{n}}{\sum\limits_{i=1}^{n} Y_i^2 - \dfrac{\left(\sum\limits_{i=1}^{n} Y_i\right)^2}{n}}$$

$$r^2 = \frac{(-2,107.14)(70,000) + 910.714(751,000) - \dfrac{(70,000)^2}{10}}{540,000,000 - \dfrac{(70,000)^2}{10}}$$

$$= \frac{46,446,414}{50,000,000} = .9289.$$

For this example 92.89% of the variation in the yearly sales volume can be explained by the variability in the number of radio commercials broadcasted per day. There is a strong linear relationship between the two variables. The linear regression model has reduced the variability in predicting sales volume by 92.89%. Only 7.11% of the variability in sales volume has to be explained by factors other than the number of radio commercials broadcasted per day.

(g) Coefficient of correlation, $r = \sqrt{r^2}$

$r = \sqrt{.9289} = .9638$. Note: r has the same sign (+ or -) as slope.

(h) Adjusted r^2

$$r^2_{adj} = 1 - \left[(1-r^2)\frac{(n-1)}{(n-2)}\right]$$

Since $r^2 = .9289$ and $n = 10$:

$$r^2_{adj} = 1 - \left[(1-.9289)\frac{(10-1)}{(10-2)}\right]$$

$$= 1 - [(.0711)(1.125)]$$

$$= .92$$

(i) Hypothesis test for the existence of a relationship between the variables.

H_0: $\beta_1 = 0$ (No relationship.)

H_1: $\beta_1 \neq 0$ (There is a relationship.)

$\alpha = .01$.

Decision rule:

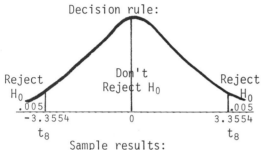

Reject H_0
.005
-3.3554
t_8

Don't
Reject H_0

0

Reject H_0
.005
3.3554
t_8

Reject H_0 if $t_8 > 3.3554$ or if $t_8 < -3.3554$. Otherwise, don't reject H_0.

Sample results:

$$b_1 = 910.714, \quad S_{b_1} = \frac{S_{YX}}{\sqrt{\sum\limits_{i=1}^{n} X_i^2 - \frac{\left(\sum\limits_{i=1}^{n} X_i\right)^2}{n}}} = \frac{666.48}{\sqrt{1,056 - \frac{(100)^2}{10}}}$$

$$= 89.0623.$$

Test statistic:

$$t_8 = \frac{b_1 - \beta_1}{S_{b_1}} = \frac{910.714 - 0}{89.0623} = 10.23$$

Conclusion: Since $t_8 = 10.23 > t_{.005} = 3.3554$ reject H_0. There is a linear relationship between radio commercials broadcasted and the sales volume. (Note: Another method for testing the existence of a relationship between the variables involves the sample correlation coefficient (r)).

(j) Confidence interval estimate of average yearly sales volume when $X_i = 8$.

$$\hat{Y}_i \pm t_{n-2} \, S_{yx} \, \sqrt{h_i}$$

where $h_i = \frac{1}{n} + \frac{(X_i - \bar{X})^2}{\sum X_i^2 - \frac{(\sum X_i)^2}{n}}$ $\hat{Y}_i = 5,179$ units (from (d)).

$$5{,}179 \pm 3.3554(666.48)\sqrt{\frac{1}{10} + \frac{(8 - 10)^2}{1{,}056 - \frac{(100)^2}{10}}}$$

$$5{,}179 \pm 3.3554(666.48)\sqrt{.10 + \frac{4}{56}} = 5{,}179 \pm 3.3554(666.48)\sqrt{.171429}$$

$$5{,}179 \pm 3.3554(666.48)(.4140) = 5{,}179 \pm 926.$$

$$4{,}253 \leq \mu_{YX} \leq 6{,}105$$

(k) Prediction interval of sales volume when X_i = 8 (for an individual city that broadcasts 8 radio commercials per day).

$$\hat{Y}_i \pm t_{n-2}\, S_{yx}\, \sqrt{1 + h_i}$$

where $h_i = \dfrac{1}{n} + \dfrac{(X - \bar{X})^2}{\displaystyle\sum_{i=1}^{n} X_i^2 - \dfrac{\left(\displaystyle\sum_{i=1}^{n} X_i\right)^2}{n}}$

$\hat{Y}_i$ = -2,107.14 + 910.714 X_i and for X_i = 8,

$\hat{Y}_i$ = 5,179 units (see (d)). Also $\bar{X}$ = 10, S_{yx} = 666.48, $\displaystyle\sum_{i=1}^{n} X_i$ = 100,

$\displaystyle\sum_{i=1}^{n} X_i^2$ = 1,056. From Table E.3 t_8 = 3.3554

Thus $\hat{Y}_i \pm t_{n-2}\, S_{yx}\, \sqrt{1 + h_i}$

so that $\hat{Y}_i \pm t_{n-2}\, S_{yx}\, \sqrt{1 + \dfrac{1}{n} + \dfrac{(X_i - \bar{X})^2}{\displaystyle\sum_{i=1}^{n} X_i^2 - \dfrac{\left(\displaystyle\sum_{i=1}^{n} X_i\right)^2}{n}}}$

and $5{,}179 \pm (3.3554)(666.48)\sqrt{1 + \dfrac{1}{10} + \dfrac{(8-10)^2}{1{,}056 - \dfrac{(100)^2}{10}}}$

$$5{,}179 \pm 2236.3069\sqrt{1 + \frac{1}{10} + \frac{(-2)^2}{1.056 - 1{,}000}}$$

$$5{,}179 \pm 2236.3069\sqrt{1.1714}$$

$$5{,}179 \pm 2420$$

Thus $2{,}759 \leq \hat{Y}_i \leq 7{,}599$ (units per year)

(1) Confidence interval for the true slope.

$$b_1 \pm t_{n-2} s_{b_1} = 910.714 \pm 3.3554(89.0623) = 910.714 \pm 298.840$$

$$611.874 \leq \beta_1 \leq 1,209.554$$

(m) Very little faith should be placed on predictions about yearly sales volume in a city which has less than 7 broadcasts or more than 14 broadcasts since they are outside the range of the observed data. There is no guarantee that the fitted line will hold outside the range of the observed data.

REVIEW PROBLEM

A record of maintenance cost is kept on 10 similar electronic calculators. The relationship between maintenance cost and age of calculators can be examined from the following data:

Electronic Calculators	X Age of Calculator (Years)	Y Maintenance Cost (Dollars)
I	9	40
II	4	12
III	2	8
IV	8	27
V	4	15
VI	5	17
VII	1	5
VIII	3	10
IX	6	25
X	8	31

(a) Set up a scatter diagram.

(b) Assuming a linear relationship, use the Least Squares method to compute the regression coefficients (b_0 and b_1).

(c) Interpret the meaning of the slope (b_1) in this problem.

(d) If the electronic calculator is 7 years old, predict the maintenance cost.

(e) Compute the standard error of estimate (S_{YX}).

(f) Compute the coefficient of determination (r^2) and interpret its meaning in this problem.

(g) Compute the coefficient of correlation.

(h) Compute the adjusted r^2.

(i) At the .05 level of significance is there evidence of a relationship between age of calculator and maintenance cost?

(j) Set up a 95% confidence interval estimate of the average maintenance cost for electronic calculators that are 7 years old.

(k) Set up a 95% confidence interval estimate of the maintenance cost of an individual electronic calculator that is 7 years old.

(l) Perform a residual analysis to determine the adequacy of the fit of the model.

SOLUTION TO REVIEW PROBLEM

Basic Computations.

The sums of the following expressions have integer (i) values from 1 to n (n=10).

$$\Sigma X_i = 50 \qquad \Sigma X_i^2 = 316 \qquad \Sigma X_i^2 - \frac{(\Sigma X_i)^2}{n} = 316 - \frac{(50)^2}{10} = 66$$

$$\Sigma Y_i = 190 \qquad \Sigma Y_i^2 = 4{,}762 \qquad \Sigma Y_i^2 - \frac{(\Sigma Y_i)^2}{n} = 4{,}762 - \frac{(190)^2}{10} = 1{,}152$$

$$\Sigma X_i Y_i = 1{,}218 \qquad \Sigma X_i Y_i - \frac{(\Sigma X_i)(\Sigma Y_i)}{n} = 1{,}218 - \frac{(50)(190)}{10} = 268$$

(a) Scatter diagram of Age of Calculator versus Maintenance Cost.

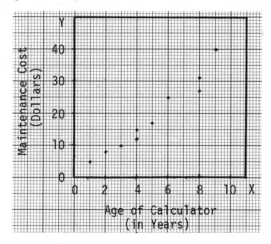

(b)
$$b_1 = \frac{\Sigma X_i Y_i - \frac{(\Sigma X_i)(\Sigma Y_i)}{n}}{\Sigma X_i^2 - \frac{(\Sigma X_i)^2}{n}} = \frac{268}{66} = 4.06061.$$

$$b_0 = \bar{Y} - b_1\bar{X} = 19 - 4.06061(5) = -1.30305.$$

$$\hat{Y}_i = -1.303 + 4.061X_i$$

(c) The maintenance cost of the electronic calculator increases by $4.061 for each one year increase in the age of the calculator.

179

(d) If $X_i = 7$, then $\hat{Y}_i = -1.303 + 4.061X_i = -1.303 + 4.061(7) = \$27.124$.

(e) $S_{YX} = \sqrt{\dfrac{\Sigma Y_i^2 - b_0 \Sigma Y_i - b_1 \Sigma X_i Y_i}{n-2}}$

$\quad = \sqrt{\dfrac{4{,}762 - (-1.30305)(190) - (4.06061)(1{,}218)}{8}}$

$\quad = \sqrt{\dfrac{63.75652}{8}} = \sqrt{7.969565} = 2.823$ dollars.

(f) $r^2 = 1 - \dfrac{\Sigma Y_i^2 - b_0 \Sigma Y_i - b_1 \Sigma X_i Y_i}{\Sigma Y_i^2 - \dfrac{(\Sigma Y_i)^2}{n}} = 1 - \dfrac{63.75652}{1{,}152} = 1 - .0553 = .9447$.

The coefficient of determination measures the proportion of variation that is explained by or is attributable to the independent variable for the regression model. For this problem 94.47% of the variability in the maintenance cost has been explained by the age of the electronic calculators.

(g) $r = \sqrt{r^2} = \sqrt{.9447} = .9720$.

(h) $r^2_{adj} = 1 - [(1-r^2)\,\dfrac{(n-1)}{(n-2)}]$

Since $r^2 = .9447$ and $n = 10$

$r^2_{adj} = 1 - [(1-.9447)\,\dfrac{(10-1)}{(10-2)}]$

$\quad = 1 - [(.0553)(1.125)]$

$\quad = .9378$

(i) H_0: $\rho = 0$ (No correlation.) Decision rule: Reject H_0 if $t_8 >$
H_1: $\rho \neq 0$ (Correlation.) 2.3060 or if $t_8 < -2.3060$. Otherwise,
$\alpha = .05$ don't reject H_0.

Sample result and test statistic:

$t_8 = \dfrac{r}{\sqrt{\dfrac{1-r^2}{n-2}}} = \dfrac{.9720}{\sqrt{\dfrac{1-.9447}{10-2}}} = \dfrac{.9720}{.0831} = 11.70$.

Conclusion: Since $t_8 = 11.70 > t_{.025} = 2.3060$, reject H_0. There appears to be a relationship between the variables at $\alpha = .05$.

(j) $\hat{Y}_i \pm t_{n-2}\, S_{yx}\, \sqrt{h_i}$

where $h_i = \dfrac{1}{n} + \dfrac{(X_i - \overline{X})^2}{\sum X_i^2 - \dfrac{(\sum X_i)^2}{n}}$

From (d), if $X_i = 7$, then $\hat{Y}_i = \$27.124$.

Thus,

$\$27.124 \pm 2.3060(2.823)\ \overline{\dfrac{1}{10} + \dfrac{(7-5)^2}{66}}$

$\$27.124 \pm 2.3060(2.823)\ \sqrt{.160606} = \$27.124 \pm 2.3060(2.823)(.4008)$

$\$27.124 \pm 2.609$

$\quad \$24.515 \leqq \mu_{yx} \leqq \$29.733$

(k) $\hat{Y}_i \pm t_{n-2}\, S_{yx}\, \sqrt{1 + h_i}$

where $h_i = \dfrac{1}{n} + \dfrac{(X - \overline{X})^2}{\displaystyle\sum_{i=1}^{n} X_i^2 - \dfrac{(\sum X_i)^2}{n}}$

From (d), if $X_i = 7$, then $\hat{Y}_i = \$27.124$

Also $\overline{X} = 5$, $S_{yx} = 2.823$, $\displaystyle\sum_{i=1}^{n} X_i = 50$, $\displaystyle\sum_{i=1}^{n} X_i^2 = 316$. From

Table E.3 $t_8 = 2.3060$. Thus,

$\hat{Y}_i \pm t_{n-2}\, S_{yx}\, \sqrt{1 + h_i}$

so that

$\hat{Y}_i \pm t_{n-2}\, S_{yx}\, \sqrt{1 + \dfrac{1}{n} + \dfrac{(X_i - \overline{X})^2}{\displaystyle\sum_{i=1}^{n} X_i^2 - \dfrac{(\sum X_i)^2}{n}}}$

and

$27.124 \pm 2.3060(2.823)\ \sqrt{1 + \dfrac{1}{10} + \dfrac{(7-5)^2}{316 - \dfrac{(50)^2}{10}}}$

$27.124 \pm 6.5098\ \sqrt{1 + \dfrac{1}{10}} = \dfrac{(2)^2}{316 - 250}$

$27.124 \pm 6.5098\ \sqrt{1.1606}$

27.124 ± 7.01

Thus, $\$20.114 \leq \hat{Y}_i \leq \$34.134$

(1) Residual analysis is a graphical approach used to evaluate the adequacy of the fitted model.

Electronic Calculator	Age (X)	Maintenance Cost			Standardized Residual (ε/S_{YX})
		Observed (Y)	Predicted $(\hat{Y})$	Residual $(\varepsilon = Y - \hat{Y})$	
I	9	40	35.246	4.754	1.684
II	4	12	14.941	-2.941	-1.042
III	2	8	6.819	1.181	.418
IV	8	27	31.185	-4.185	-1.482
V	4	15	14.941	.059	.021
VI	5	17	19.002	-2.002	- .709
VII	1	5	2.758	2.242	.794
VIII	3	10	10.880	- .880	- .312
IX	6	25	23.063	1.937	.686
X	8	31	31.185	- .185	- .066

Scatter plot of standardized residuals versus age of calculator.

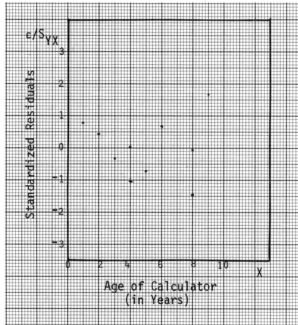

The standardized residuals have been plotted against the independent variable (age of calculator). From this graph we observe that there is a widespread scatter in the residual plot, there is no apparent pattern or relationship between the standardized residuals and the age of calculator. The standardized residuals appear to be evenly spread above and below zero and within + 2, for the differing values of age of calculator. Therefore, we may conclude that the fitted model appears to describe the data adequately.

Multiple Regression Models

In our discussion of regression and correlation we have focused upon a linear relationship between one independent variable and a dependent variable. The basic concepts of regression and correlation can be extended to a multiple regression model that involves several independent variables. In multiple regression, not only can we determine the relationship of the set of independent variables with a dependent variable, but we can assess the contribution of each independent variable to the model. In this manner, we can determine which of several alternative models is most appropriate from the point of view of both simplicity and goodness of fit. In addition to the evaluation of several independent variables, we may also wish to fit relationships that are not linear between an independent and dependent variable. Moreover, we may wish to use dummy variables in order to develop multiple regression models in which at least one of the independent variables is qualitative. The chapter concludes with an example of model building through stepwise regression using computer packages.

MULTIPLE CHOICE

1. In a multiple regression problem involving two independent variables, if b_1 is computed to be +2.0, it means that

    (a) the relationship between X_1 and Y is significant.
    (b) Y increases by 2 units for each increase of one unit of X_1 holding X_2 constant.
    (c) Y increases by 2 units for each increase of one unit of X_1 without regard to X_2.
    (d) the value of Y is 2 when X_1 equals 0.

2. If a sample of size 20 is selected for a multiple regression problem with two independent variables, the number of degrees of freedom involved in the test of the relationship of the two independent variables is _____ provided that both independent variables are quantitative.

(a) 2, 17　　　　　　　　　　(c) 18
(b) 3, 18　　　　　　　　　　(d) 17

3. The coefficient of multiple determination $(r_{Y.12}^2)$

(a) measures the variation around the predicted regression equation.
(b) measures the proportion of the variation in Y that is explained by X_1 and X_2.
(c) measures the proportion of the variation in Y that is explained by X_1 holding X_2 constant.
(d) will have the same sign as b_1.

4. The contribution of an independent variable to a multiple regression model

(a) represents the effect of adding a particular variable after other variables are included in the model.
(b) can be computed as the difference between the regression sum of squares in two different models.
(c) can be computed if the standard error of the regression coefficient is known.
(d) All of the above.

5. If a multiple regression model contains a qualitative independent variable with 3 categories, the number of dummy variables needed to represent these categories is

(a) 0.　　　　　　　　　　(c) 2.
(b) 1.　　　　　　　　　　(d) 3.

6. The coefficient of partial determination $(r_{Y1.2}^2)$

(a) measures the variation around the predicted regression equation.
(b) measures the proportion of the variation in Y that is explained by X_1 and X_2.
(c) measures the proportion of the variation in Y that is explained by X_1 holding X_2 constant.
(d) will have the same sign as b_1.

7. An educational psychologist would like to predict a child's IQ score. Data are available that include the age, grade, and achievement scores of 50 children. Which is (are) the dependent variable(s) in this situation?

(a) the child's IQ score.
(b) the child's age, grade, and achievement score.
(c) the child's age.
(d) the child's achievement score and IQ score.

8. This educational psychologist reports a $r_{y.123}^2 = -.2675$. This is

    (a) possible, but highly unlikely.
    (b) impossible.
    (c) probably due to the fact that the children in the sample had extremely low achievement test scores.
    (d) probably due to the fact that a much larger sample size was needed.

9. At this point, the "statistically oriented" educational psychologist should

    (a) report the $r_{y.123}^2 = -.2675$ and interpret it in a meaningful way that is easily understood.
    (b) recompute the $r_{y.123}^2$.
    (c) notify his boss of the $r_{y.123}^2 = -.2675$ <u>before</u> publishing the result in the community.
    (d) Perform an empirical study correlating the children's achievement test scores with their scores two years ago.

EXAMPLES

I. A shampoo company wants to study the amount of sales (Y) with respect to advertising expenditures (X_1) such as spot commercials on radio and television, ads in newspapers and magazines, etc. and promotional expenditures (X_2) such as samples sent out to prospective customers, free items attached to their products, etc.. The following data show sales, advertising expenditures and promotional expenditures in millions of dollars over the past 10 time periods.

Time Period	Sales in Time Period (Y)	Advertising Expenditure (X_1)	Promotional Expenditure (X_2)
1	39.9	6.1	1.6
2	41.4	7.1	1.4
3	49.1	12.6	.5
4	49.5	10.1	3.0
5	57.5	13.3	.6
6	59.0	13.1	3.7
7	64.9	13.8	2.7
8	56.6	10.1	8.7
9	60.2	11.5	6.4
10	57.4	10.5	6.2

(a) Assuming that each independent variable (advertising expenditure and promotional expenditure) is linearly related to sales, use the least squares method to find the multiple regression coefficients (b_0, b_1, b_2).

(b) Interpret the meaning of the slopes in this example.

(c) Predict the sales when the advertising expentiture is 11.0 and the promotional expenditure is 4.5 (millions of dollars).

(d) Determine whether there is a significant relationship between sales and the two independent variables (advertising and promotional expenditures) at the .01 level of significance.

(e) Compute the standard error of the estimate (S_{yx}), the coefficient of multiple determination $(r_{y.12}^2)$, the adjusted (r_{adj}^2), and the coefficient of correlation $(r_{y.12})$. Interpret the meaning of $r_{y.12}^2$ and r_{adj}^2 in this example.

(f) At the .01 level of significance, determine whether each independent variable makes a contribution to the regression model. Bases upon these results, indicate the regression model that should be used in this example.

(g) Compute the coefficients of partial determination $(r_{y1.1}^2$ and $r_{y2.1}^2)$ and interpret their meaning in this example.

(h) Is there any reason to "suspect" any multicollineanity in the data? Explain.

SOLUTION

I.   Parts of this example will be solved by the SPSS New Regression.

(a)

------------------------------- VARIABLES IN THE EQUATION -------------------------------

VARIABLE	B	SE B	BETA	T	SIG T
X_1 = ADVTG	b_1= 2.64580	S_{b_1}= 0.37399	0.83568	7.074	0.0002
X_2 = PROM	b_2= 1.34311	S_{b_2}= 0.35173	0.45107	3.819	0.0066
(CONSTANT)	.= 20.24838	S_{b_0}= 4.32681		4.680	0.0023

(b) The slope of the advertising expenditure with sales (b_1), computed as 2.64580 can be interpreted to mean that for a given promotional expenditure, the sales will increase $2,645,800 for each one million dollar increase in advertising expenditure. Furthermore, the slope of the promotional expenditure with sales (b_2), computed as 1.34311

186

can be interpreted to mean that for a given advertising expenditure, the sales will increase $1,343,110 for each one million dollar increase in promotional advertising.

(c) For X_1 = 11.0 (millions of dollars) and X_2 = 4.5 (millions of dollars),

$\hat{Y}_i$ = 20.24838 + 2.64580X_{1i} + 1.34311X_{2i} = 20.24838 + 2.64580(11) +

1.34311(4.5) = 55.39618 millions of dollars.

(d) H_0: $\beta_1 = \beta_2 = 0$

H_1: $\beta_1 \neq \beta_2 \neq 0$ (At least one regression coefficient is not equal to zero.)

α = .01.

Decision rule:

Reject H_0 if $F_{2,7}$ > 9.55. Otherwise, don't reject H_0.

Sample results and test statistic:

ANALYSIS OF VARIANCE

	DF	SUM OF SQUARES	MEAN SQUARE
REGRESSION	2	$SS(b_1 \& b_2)$= 552.78704	276.39352
RESIDUAL	7	59.83807	s^2_{yx}=8.54830

F = 32.33317   SIGNIF F = 0.0003

Conclusion: Since $F_{2,7}$ = 32.3332 exceeds the critical value (9.55), reject H_0. The shampoo company may conclude that at least one of the independent variables (advertising expenditure and/or promotional expenditure) is related to sales at the .01 level of significance.

(e) MULTIPLE R $r_{y.12}$=0.94991
     R SQUARE   0.90233 ← $r^2_{y.12}$

     STANDARD ERROR s_{yx}= 2.92375

$$r^2_{adj} = 1 - [(1-r^2) \frac{(n-1)}{(n-p-1)}]$$

187

where p is the number of explanatory variables in the regression equation.

Thus for our data, since r^2 = .90233, n = 10, and p = 2

$$r^2_{adj} = 1 - [(1-.90233)\frac{(10-1)}{(10-2-1)}]$$

$$= 1 - [(.09767)(1.2857142)]$$

$$= .8744243$$

In this example 90.23% of the variation in sales can be explained by the advertising and promotional expenditures.

87.44% of the variation in sales can be explained by our multiple regression model adjusted for number of predictors and sample size.

(f) (1) Contribution of X_1.

H_0: Advertising expenditure (X_1) does not significantly improve the model once promotional expenditure (X_2) has already been included. (i.e. $\beta_1 = 0$.)

H_1: Advertising expenditure significantly improves the model once promotional expenditure has already been included. (i.e. $\beta_1 \neq 0$.)

$\alpha = .01$.

Decision rule:

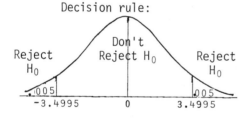

Reject H_0 if $t_7 < -3.4995$ or if $t_7 > 3.4995$. Otherwise, don't reject H_0.

Sample results and test statistic:

--------------------- VARIABLES IN THE EQUATION ---------------------

VARIABLE	B	SE B	BETA	T	SIG T
X_1=ADVTG	b_1= 2.64580	S_{b_1}=0.37399	0.83568	* 7.074	0.0002
X_2=PROM	b_2= 1.34311	S_{b_2}=0.35173	0.45107	** 3.819	0.0066
(CONSTANT)	b_0=20.24838	S_{b_0}=4.32681		4.680	0.0023

*Note: $t = \dfrac{b_1 - \beta_1}{S_{b_1}} = \dfrac{2.64580 - 0}{.37399} = 7.074$.

Conclusion: Since the computed t = 7.074 exceeds the critical value (3.4995), reject H_0. The addition of advertising expenditure significantly improves the multiple regression model that already contains promotional expenditure.

188

(2) Contribution of X_2.

H_0: Promotional expenditure does not significantly improve the model once advertising expenditure has already been included. (i.e. $\beta_2 = 0$.)

H_1: Promotional expenditure significantly improves the model once advertising expenditure has already been included. (i.e. $\beta_2 \neq 0$.)

$\alpha = .01$.

Decision rule: same as in (f)(1).

Sample results and test statistic:

**Note: $t = \dfrac{b_2 - \beta_2}{S_{b_2}} = \dfrac{1.343110 - 0}{.35173} = 3.819$. (See printout in part (f)(1).)

Conclusion: Since $t = 3.819$ exceeds $t = 3.4995$, reject H_0. The addition of promotional expenditure significantly improves the multiple regression model that already contains advertising expenditure.

The multiple regression model should include both advertising expenditure and promotional expenditure in predicting sales, since the contribution of each of the two independent variables after the other was already included in the model was significant.

(g)

$$SS(b_1 | b_2) = \frac{b_1^2 S_{YX}^2}{S_{b_1}^2} = \frac{(2.64580)^2 (8.54830)}{(.37399)^2} = 427.83253.$$

$$SS(b_2 | b_1) = \frac{b_2^2 S_{YX}^2}{S_{b_2}^2} = \frac{(1.34311)^2 (8.54830)}{(.35173)^2} = 124.64765.$$

SST $= 552.78704 + 59.83807 = 612.62511$ (from printout part (d)).

$SS(b_1$ and $b_2) = 552.78704$ (from printout part (d)).

$$r_{Y1.2}^2 = \frac{SS(b_1 | b_2)}{SS_{TOT} - SS(b_1 \text{ and } b_2) + SS(b_1 | b_2)}$$

$$= \frac{427.83253}{612.62511 - 552.78704 + 427.83253} = .87730.$$

$$r_{Y2.1}^2 = \frac{SS(b_2 | b_1)}{SS_{TOT} - SS(b_1 \text{ and } b_2) + SS(b_2 | b_1)}$$

$$= \frac{124.64765}{612.62511 - 552.78704 + 124.64765} = .67565.$$

The coefficient of partial determination of variable sales with advertising expenditure while holding promotional expenditure constant $(r_{Y1.2}^2)$ may be interpreted to mean that for a fixed promotional expenditure 87.73% of the variation in sales is explained by advertising expenditure. Furthermore, the coefficient of partial determination of variable sales with promotional expenditure while holding advertising expenditure constant $(r_{Y2.1}^2)$ may be interpreted to mean that for a fixed advertising expenditure 67.565% of the variation in sales is explained by promotional expenditure.

(h) We measure for collinearity using the variance inflationary factor (VIF) which can be obtained as output from various computer packages.

$$VIF_j = \frac{1}{1-R_j^2}$$

where R_j^2 represents the coefficient of multiple determination of explanatory variable j with all other X variables. (Please remember that when there are only two explanatory variables, R_j^2 is simply the coefficient of determination between X_1 and X_2).

$$VIF_1 = VIF_2 = \frac{1}{1-(.007705)^2}$$

$$VIF_1 = VIF_2 \cong 1$$

As a rule of thumb, if $VIF_j > 10$, there is too much correlation between variable X_j and the other explanatory variables. Therefore, we may conclude that there is no reason to suspect any multicollinearity between advertising expenditures and promotional expenditures.

II. A certain economist theorizes that housing demand (in thousands) can be predicted by median disposable income (in thousands of dollars) and location of community (0 = Northeast and 1 = Southwest). Through several government agencies he has compiled the following set of data for 12 communities of the same size:

Community	Median Disposable Income (X_1)	Location (X_2)	Housing Demand (Y)
1	6.3	1	1.0
2	6.6	1	1.0
3	7.3	1	1.2
4	7.1	1	1.1
5	7.5	0	1.1
6	7.2	0	1.0
7	7.3	1	1.1
8	7.1	1	1.0
9	7.1	0	.9
10	6.7	0	.8
11	6.3	0	.7
12	6.7	0	.8

Use the computer package SAS to perform a multiple linear regression analysis.

(a) Based upon the results obtained state the multiple regression equation.

(b) Interpret the meaning of the slopes in this example.

(c) Predict housing demand when the median disposable income is 7.0 (thousands of dollars) and the community is located in the Northeast.

(d) Interpret the meaning of the coefficient of multiple determination $r_{Y.12}^2$.

(e) Determine whether there is a relationship between housing demand and the two independent variables (median disposable income and location) at the .05 level of significance. Find the P-value.

(f) At the .05 level of significance determine whether each independent variable makes a contribution to the regression model. Based upon these results, indicate the regression model that should be utilized in this example.

SOLUTION

(a)

PARAMETER	ESTIMATE	T FOR HO: PARAMETER=0	STD ERROR OF ESTIMATE
INTERCEPT	b_0 = -0.80987713	-2.45	s_{b_0} = 0.33041017
X_1 = DISPINC	b_1 = 0.24480151	5.14	s_{b_1} = 0.04762409
X_2 = LOC	b_2 = 0.17517328	4.79	s_{b_2} = 0.03654630

Assuming the slope between housing demand and median disposable income is the same for both locations, the regression model could be stated as

$$\hat{Y}_i = -.80987713 + .24480151X_{1i} + .17517328X_{2i}.$$

(b) The slope of the median disposable income with housing demand (b_1), is computed as .24480151. This can be interpreted to mean that when the effect of location is held constant housing demand will increase by 244.80151 for each additional $1,000 in median disposable income. The slope of location (β_2) measures the effect on housing demand of a community being located in the Southwest (X_2=1) as compared to the Northeast (X_2=0). Thus when median disposable income is held constant, the average housing demand in a Southwest community would be 175.17328 higher than that in a corresponding Northeast community.

(c) For X_1 = 7.0 (thousands of dollars) and X_2 = 0 (Northeast),

$$\hat{Y}_i = -.80987713 + .24480151X_{1i} + .17517328X_{2i}$$

$$= -.80987713 + .24480151(7.0) + .17517328(0)$$

$$= .90373344 \text{ (in thousands) or } 903.73344.$$

(d)

R-SQUARE

$$r^2_{y.12} \quad 0.851571$$

In this example 85.16% of the variation in housing demand is explained by median disposable income and location.

(e) Hypothesis test for the relationship between the dependent variable and the independent variables.

H_0: $\beta_1 = \beta_2 = 0$ (There is no relationship between housing demand and the median disposable income and location.)

H_1: $\beta_1 \neq \beta_2 \neq 0$ (At least one regression coefficient is not equal to zero.)

$\alpha = .05$.

Decision rule:

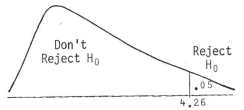

Don't
Reject H_0

Reject
H_0

.05

4.26

Reject H_0 if $F_{2,9} > 4.26$. Otherwise don't reject H_0.

Sample results and test statistic:

Analysis of Variance Table for testing the significance of the two regression coefficients.

SOURCE	DF	SUM OF SQUARES	MEAN SQUARE	F VALUE
MODEL	2	$SS(b_1 \& b_2)$= 0.20650599	0.10325299	25.82
ERROR	9	0.03599401	S^2_{yx}=0.00399933	PR > F
CORRECTED TOTAL	11	0.24250000		0.0002

Conclusion: Since F = 25.82 exceeds the critical F value (4.26), reject H_0. The economist may conclude that at least one of the independent variables (median disposable income and/or location) is related to housing demand at the .05 level of significance.

The P-value for this example is .0002.

(f) Determination of the contribution of each independent variable.

(1) Contribution of X_1.

H_0: Median disposable income does not significantly improve the model once location of community has already been included. (i.e. $\beta_1 = 0$.)

H_1: Median disposable income does significantly improve the model once location of community has already been included. (i.e. $\beta_1 \neq 0$.)

$\alpha = .05$.

Decision rule:

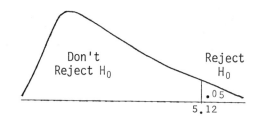

Reject H_0 if $F_{1,9} > 5.12$. Otherwise don't reject H_0.

Sample results and test statistic:

SOURCE	DF	TYPE IV SS	F VALUE
X_1 = DISPINC	1	$SS(b_1|b_2) = 0.10567265$	26.42
X_2 = LOC	1	$SS(b_2|b_1) = 0.09188334$	22.97

(Note: $F_{1,9} = \dfrac{SSR\ (b_1|b_2)}{S_{YX}^2} = \dfrac{.10567265}{.00399933} = 26.42.$)

Conclusion: Since the computed $F_{1,9} = 26.42$ is greater than the critical value (5.12), reject H_0. The addition of X_1 (median disposable income) significantly improves the multiple regression model that already contains variable X_2 (location).

(2) Contribution of X_2.

H_0: Location of community does not significantly improve the model once median disposable income has already been included. (i.e. $\beta_2 = 0$.)

H_1: Location of community significantly improves the model once median disposable income has already been included. (i.e. $\beta_2 \neq 0$.)

$\alpha = .05$.

Decision rule: Same as in part (f) (1).

Sample results and test statistic:

SOURCE	DF	TYPE IV SS	F VALUE
X_1 = DISPINC	1	$SS(b_1|b_2) = 0.10567265$	26.42
X_2 = LOC	1	$SS(b_2|b_1) = 0.09188334$	22.97

(Note: $F_{1,9} = \dfrac{SSR\ (b_2|b_1)}{S_{YX}^2} = \dfrac{.09188334}{.00399933} = 22.97.$)

Conclusion: Since the computed $F_{1,9} = 22.97$ exceeds the critical value (5.12), reject H_0. The addition of variable X_2 (location) significantly improves the multiple regression model that already contains variable X_1 (median disposable income).

The multiple regression model should include both median disposable income and location of community in predicting housing demand since the contribution of each of the two independent variables after the other was included in the model was significant. Assuming the slope between housing demand and median disposable income is the same for the two locations the model for these data may be stated as

$$\hat{Y}_i = -.80987713 + .24480151X_{1i} + .17517328X_{2i}$$

so that for the communities in the Northeast ($X_2 = 0$),

$$\hat{Y}_i = -.80987713 + .24480151X_{1i}$$

while for the communities in the Southwest ($X_2 = 1$),

$$\hat{Y}_i = -.80987713 + .24480151X_{1i} + .17517328(1)$$

$$\hat{Y}_i = -.63470385 + .24480151X_{1i}.$$

III. An educational psychologist wishes to develop a model to predict the hours spent studying on statistics grades. Consider the following data set obtained from 9 students in her class:

Student	X Hours Spent Studying	Y Statistics Grade
1	0	20
2	5	57
3	10	82
4	15	91
5	20	81
6	25	85
7	30	74
8	35	67
9	40	64

(a) Calculate the curvilinear regression equation.

(b) Calculate the curvilinear regression equation using the centering method.

(c) Which method is more appropriate in this example? Why?

SOLUTION

Parts of this example will be solved using Minitab.

Presented below is a scatter plot of "grade" with "studyhrs":

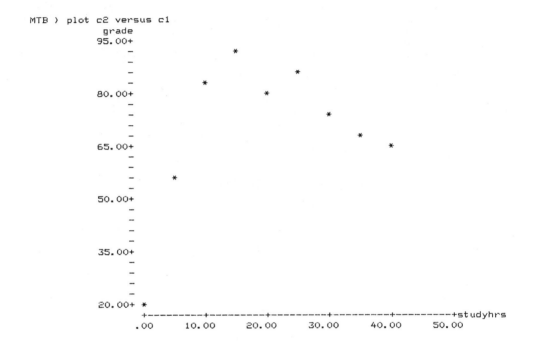

(a) Calculating the curvilinear regression equation:

$$\hat{Y} = b_0 + b_1 X + b_{11} X^2$$

```
MTB > let c3 = c1*c1
MTB > name c3 = 'timesq'
MTB > print c2 c1 c3
 ROW   grade   studyhrs   timesq
         Y         X        X²
   1     20        0         0
   2     57        5        25
   3     82       10       100
   4     91       15       225
   5     81       20       400
   6     85       25       625
   7     74       30       900
   8     67       35      1225
   9     64       40      1600
```

```
MTB > regress c2 on 2 in c1 c3;
MTB > vif.
```

THE REGRESSION EQUATION IS
grade = 30.1 + 5.18 studyhrs − 0.114 timesq
  Y   X   X²

COLUMN	COEFFICIENT	ST. DEV. OF COEF.	T-RATIO = COEF/S.D.	V.I.F.
	30.067 b_0	7.946	3.78	
studyhrs X	5.1848 b_1	0.9263	5.60	13.5
timesq X²	−0.11429 b_{11}	0.02228	−5.13	13.5

$S = 9.776 = S_{yx}$

R-SQUARED = 84.3 PERCENT
R-SQUARED = 79.1 PERCENT, ADJUSTED FOR D.F.

(b) Calculating the curvilinear regression equation using the centering method:

$$\hat{Y} = b_0^1 + b_1^1 (X-\overline{X}) + b_{11}^1 (X-\overline{X})^2$$

```
MTB > describe c2 c1 c3
```

	Y grade	X studyhrs	X² timesq
N	9	9	9
MEAN	69.0	20.0 = $\overline{X}$	567
MEDIAN	74.0	20.0	400
TMEAN	69.0	20.0	567
STDEV	21.4	13.7	569
SEMEAN	7.1	4.6	190
MAX	91.0	40.0	1600
MIN	20.0	0.0	0
Q3	83.5	32.5	1062
Q1	60.5	7.5	62

```
MTB > let c4 = c1 - 20.0
MTB > let c5 = c4*c4
MTB > name c4 = 'hourscen' c5 = 'timesqc'
MTB > print c2 c1 c4 c3 c5
```

ROW	grade Y	studyhrs X	hourscen $(X-\bar{X})$	timesq X^2	timesqc $(X-\bar{X})^2$
1	20	0	−20	0	400
2	57	5	−15	25	225
3	82	10	−10	100	100
4	91	15	−5	225	25
5	81	20	0	400	0
6	85	25	5	625	25
7	74	30	10	900	100
8	67	35	15	1225	225
9	64	40	20	1600	400

```
MTB > regress c2 on 2 in c4 c5;
MTB > vif.
```

THE REGRESSION EQUATION IS

grade = 88.0 + 0.613 hourscen − 0.114 timesqc
  Y $(X-\bar{X})$ $(X-\bar{X})^2$

COLUMN	COEFFICIENT	ST. DEV. OF COEF.	T-RATIO = COEF/S.D.	V.I.F.
	88.048 b_0	4.941	17.82	
hourscen $(X-\bar{X})$	0.6133 b_1	0.2524	2.43	1.0
timesqc $(X-\bar{X})^2$	−0.11429 b_{11}	0.02228	−5.13	1.0

$S = 9.776$ S_{yx}

R-SQUARED = 84.3 PERCENT
R-SQUARED = 79.1 PERCENT, ADJUSTED FOR D.F.

ANALYSIS OF VARIANCE

DUE TO	DF	SS	MS=SS/DF
REGRESSION	2	3078.6	1539.3
RESIDUAL	6	573.4	95.6
TOTAL	8	3652.0	

FURTHER ANALYSIS OF VARIANCE
SS EXPLAINED BY EACH VARIABLE WHEN ENTERED IN THE ORDER GIVEN

DUE TO	DF	SS
REGRESSION	2	3078.6
hourscen	1	564.3
timesqc	1	2514.3

(c) As in this example, the centering method is usually more appropriate when fitting quadratic (i.e., second degree) regression models. Mathematically, the two regression equations -- centered, and uncentered -- are equivalent. They give the same values for $\hat{Y}$ and they explain the same amount of the total variation. (Note the r^2, r^2_{adj}, and S_{yx} terms). Moreover, the b_{11} and b^1_{11} coefficients and their respective standard errors are also identical. The difference in the two models then occurs in the b_0 versus b^1_0 and b_1 versus b^1_1 terms -- along with their respective standard errors. However, the centered model usually permits a more realistic interpretation of these coefficients. The problem of multicollinearity caused by the high correlation between the X and X^2 terms is reduced dramatically when the centered model is used. We note here that the VIF changes from 13.5 to 1.0 and $S_{b^1_1}$ is greatly deflated when compared to S_{b_1}.

Evaluating the contribution of the linear component to the centered curvilinear regression model, we note that t=2.43 is not quite significiant at the α = .05 level ($t_{.95,6}$ = 2.4469). Moreover, the ratio of the two (absolute) t-values -- $|t_{linear}|/|t_{curvilinear}|$ = 2.43/5.13 = .47 demonstrates that in our centered model the curvilinear term is the one of real importance. Its t value is more than twice as large as the other. On the other hand, an examination of this ratio in our uncentered model, 5.60/5.13 - 1.09, would lead us to falsely conclude that the two coefficients are equally important -- again illustrating the utility of the centering technique.

REVIEW PROBLEM

A study was conducted by the driving institute relating mileage (Y) in miles per gallon to air temperature (X_1) and vehicle weight (X_2). Ten randomly selected vehicles were driven under identical urban conditions with the following data collected.

Vehicle Number	X_1 Temperature (^{0}F)	X_2 Weight (pounds)	Y Mileage
1	26	2,800	18.33
2	65	3,700	15.91
3	65	3,600	16.37
4	50	3,200	17.50
5	45	4,100	15.52
6	35	2,600	18.85
7	40	3,600	16.79
8	85	3,400	16.45
9	35	3,800	16.51
10	85	2,700	17.88

(a) Assuming that each independent variable (air temperature and vehicle weight) is related linearly to mileage, use the least squares method to find the multiple regression coefficients (b_0, b_1, b_2).

(b) Interpret the meaning of the slopes in this problem.

(c) Predict the mileage when the air temperature is 50° F. and the vehicle weight is 3,200 pounds.

(d) Determine whether there is a significant relationship between mileage and the two independent variables (temperature and weight) at the .05 level of significance. Find the P-value for this problem.

(e) Interpret the meaning of the coefficient of multiple determination ($r_{Y.12}^2$) in this problem.

(f) At the .05 level of significance, determine whether each independent variable makes a contribution to the regression model. Based upon these results, indicate the regression model that should be used in this problem.

(g) Set up a 95% confidence interval estimate of the average mileage per gallon when the air temperature is 50° F. and the vehicle weight is 3,200 pounds.

(h) Set up a 95% confidence interval estimate of the true population slope between mileage and air temperature.

(i) Compute the coefficients of partial determination ($r_{Y1.2}^{2}$ and $r_{Y2.1}^{2}$) and interpret their meaning in this problem.

SOLUTION REVIEW PROBLEM

Parts of this problem will be solved by SAS GLM.

(a)

PARAMETER	ESTIMATE	T FOR H0: PARAMETER=0	STD ERROR OF ESTIMATE
INTERCEPT	b_0= 24.60292908	71.42	S_{b_0}= 0.34446352
X_1 = TEMP	b_1= -0.01479896	-6.43	S_{b_1}= 0.00230210
X_2 = WEIGHT	b_2= -0.00203167	-21.40	S_{b_2}= 0.00009495

Multiple Regression Equation:

$$\hat{Y}_i = 24.60292908 - .01479896X_{1i} - .00203167X_{2i}.$$

(b) The slope of the air temperature ($^\circ$F.) with mileage (b_1), computed as -.01479896, can be interpreted to mean that for a vehicle with a given weight (in pounds), the mileage will decrease .01479896 miles per gallon for each increase in air temperature of 1°F. Furthermore, the slope of the weight of the vehicle with mileage (b_2), computed as -.00203167, can be interpreted to mean that for a given air temperature the mileage will decrease by .00203167 miles per gallon for each additional pound of vehicle.

(c) Prediction of the dependent variable, $\hat{Y}_i$, for given values of the independent variables.

$$\hat{Y}_i = 24.60292908 - .01479896X_{1i} - .00203167X_{2i}.$$

For $X_{1i} = 50^\circ$F. and $X_{2i} = 3,200$ pounds,

$$\hat{Y}_i = 24.60292908 - .01479896(50) - .00203167(3,200)$$

$$\hat{Y}_i = 17.36163708 \text{ miles per gallon.}$$

(d) Hypothesis test for the relationship between the dependent variable and the independent variables.

H_0: $\beta_1 = \beta_2 = 0$ (There is no relationship between mileage and the vehicle weight and air temperature.)

H_1: $\beta_1 \neq \beta_2 \neq 0$ (At least one regression coefficient is not equal to zero.)

$\alpha = .05.$

Decision rule:

202

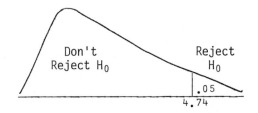

Don't Reject H_0 Reject H_0

.05
4.74

Reject H_0 if $F_{2,7} > 4.74$. Otherwise, don't reject H_0.

Sample results and test statistic:

Analysis of Variance Table for testing the significance of the two regression coefficients.

SOURCE	DF	SUM OF SQUARES	MEAN SQUARE	F VALUE
MODEL	2	$SS(b_1 \& b_2)=$ 10.42997672	5.21498836	248.82
ERROR	7	0.14671328	$S^2_{yx}=$ 0.02095904	PR > F
CORRECTED TOTAL	9	10.57669000		0.0001

Conclusion: Since $F_{2,7}$ = 248.82 exceeds the critical value (4.74), reject H_0. The driving institute may conclude that at least one of the independent variables (temperature and/or weight) is related to mileage at the .05 level of significance.

The P-value in this problem is .0001.

(e)

R-SQUARE

$$r^2_{y.12} = 0.986129$$

The coefficient of multiple determination represents the proportion of the variation in mileage (dependent variable) that is explained by air temperature and vehicle weight (independent variables). In this problem, 98.6129% of the variation in mileage can be explained by the air temperature and vehicle weight.

(f) Determination of the contribution of each independent variable.

(1) Contribution of X_1.

H_0: Temperature (X_1) does not significantly improve the model once vehicle weight (X_2) has already been included. (i.e. $\beta_1 = 0$.)

H_1: Temperature significantly improves the model once vehicle weight has already been included. (i.e. $\beta_1 \neq 0$.)

α = .05.

Decision rule:

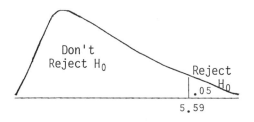

Don't
Reject H_0

Reject H_0
.05

5.59

Reject H_0 if $F_{1,7} > 5.59$. Otherwise, don't reject H_0.

Sample results and test statistic:

SOURCE	DF	TYPE IV SS	F VALUE
X_1 = TEMP	1	$SS(b_1|b_2) = 0.86613145$	41.32
X_2 = WEIGHT	1	$SS(b_2|b_1) = 9.59657438$	457.87

$$F_{1,7} = \frac{SSR\ (b_1|b_2)}{S_{YX}^2} = \frac{.86613145}{.02095904} = 41.32.$$

(Note: Since $t_{n-3}^2 = F_{1,n-3}$ an equivalent test for the contribution of each independent variable would be the t for regression coefficient--

i.e. $t = \dfrac{b_1 - \beta_1}{S_{b_1}} = \dfrac{-.014798960 - 0}{.00230210} = -6.43$. See printout part (a).)

Conclusion: Since the computed F = 41.32 exceeds the critical F = 5.59, reject H_0. (Similarly, since t = -6.43 is less than the critical value (-2.3646), reject H_0.) The addition of variable X_1 (air temperature) significantly improves the multiple regression model that already contains variable X_2 (vehicle weight).

(2) Contribution of X_2.

H_0: Vehicle weight does not significantly improve the model once air temperature has already been included. (i.e. $\beta_2 = 0$.)

H_1: Vehicle weight significantly improves the model once air temperature has already been included. (i.e. $\beta_2 \neq 0$.)

$\alpha = .05$.

Decision rule: Same as in (f) (1).

Sample results and test statistic:

$$F_{1,7} = \frac{SSR\ (b_2|b_1)}{S_{YX}^2} = \frac{9.59657438}{.02095904} = 457.87.\quad \text{(See printout in (f)(1))}$$

Conclusion: Since the computed F = 457.87 exceeds the critical value (5.59), reject H_0. The addition of variable X_2 (vehicle weight) significantly improves the multiple regression model that already contains variable X_1 (air temperature).

The multiple regression model should include both air temperature and vehicle weight in predicting mileage since the contribution of each of the two independent variables after the other was already included in the model was significant.

(g) Confidence interval estimates for predicting μ_{YX} are given for each observation in the sample by the SAS GLM procedure.

OBSERVATION	PREDICTED VALUE	LOWER 95% CL FOR MEAN	UPPER 95% CL FOR MEAN
1	18.52947199	18.30824915	18.75069482
2	16.12380683	15.97498147	16.27263219
3	16.32697412	16.18874292	16.46520532
➤ 4	17.36162772	17.24697705	17.47627839
5	15.60711695	15.40234267	15.81189123
6	18.80261589	18.57907184	19.02615994
7	16.69694820	16.55584809	16.83804831
8	16.43732943	16.23233452	16.64232433
9	16.36460844	16.18706748	16.54214940
10	17.85950044	17.60873977	18.11026111

The 95% confidence interval estimate of the average miles per gallon when X_1 = 50°F. and X_2 = 3,200 pounds is

$$17.24697705 \leqq \mu_{YX} \leqq 17.47627839.$$

(h) Confidence interval estimate for β_1. $(b_1 \pm t_{n-p-1}S_{b_1})$

$$-.01479896 \pm 2.3646(.00230210) = -.01479896 \pm .00544355$$
$$-.02024251 \leqq \beta_1 \leqq -.00935541$$

(i) Coefficient of Partial Determination.

$$r_{Y1.2}{}^2 = \frac{SSR\ (b_1|b_2)}{SST\ -\ SSR\ (b_1\ and\ b_2)\ +\ SSR\ (b_1|b_2)}$$

and

$$r_{Y2.1}{}^2 = \frac{SSR\ (b_2|b_1)}{SST\ -\ SSR\ (b_1\ and\ b_2)\ +\ SSR\ (b_2|b_1)}$$

where

SSR $(b_1|b_2)$ = Sum of squares of the contribution of variable X_1 to the regression model given that variable X_2 is already included in the model = .86613145 (from printout in part (f)--Type IV SS).

SST = Total sum of squares for Y = SSR (b_1 and b_2) + SSE = 10.42997672 + .14671328 = 10.57669000 (from printout in part (d)).

SSR (b_1 and b_2) = Regression sum of squares when variables X_1 and X_2 are both included in the multiple regression model = 10.42997672 (from printout in part (d)).

SSR ($b_2|b_1$) = Sum of squares of the contribution of variable X_2 to the regression model given that variable X_1 is already included in the model = 9.59657438 (from printout in part (f)--Type IV SS).

$$r_{Y1.2}^2 = \frac{.86613145}{10.57669000 - 10.42997672 + .86613145} = .855147$$

$$r_{Y2.1}^2 = \frac{9.59657438}{10.57669000 - 10.42997672 + 9.59657438} = .984942.$$

The coefficient of partial determination of variable mileage (Y) with air temperature (X_1) while holding vehicle weight (X_2) constant ($r_{Y1.2}^2$) can be interpreted to mean that for a fixed vehicle weight, 85.51% of the variation in mileage can be explained by the variation in air temperature. Similarly, the coefficient of partial determination of mileage (Y) with vehicle weight (X_2) while holding air temperature (X_1) constant ($r_{Y2.1}^2$) can be interpreted to mean that for a fixed air temperature, 98.49% of the variation in mileage can be explained by the variation in vehicle weight.

18

Index Numbers, Time Series, and Business Forecasting

Over the years index numbers have become increasingly important to business and government leaders as indicators of changing economic or business activity. In fact, the use of index numbers has become the most widely accepted procedure for measuring changes in business conditions. Thus,the first part of this chapter focuses upon the concepts of index number construction. In particular, the development and use of various price indexes are considered and the importance of the well-known Consumer Price Index is described. In addition, such concepts as aggregate price indexes versus mean price relatives, nominal versus real wages, and index number adjustments are discussed.

The second part of this chapter focuses on time series analysis. Since economic and business conditions vary over time, business leaders must find ways to keep abreast of the effects that such changes will have on their particular operations. One such method which business leaders may use as an aid in controlling present operations and in planning for future needs (by forecasting likely developments in sales, raw materials, etc.) is time-series analysis. The basic assumption of classical time-series analysis is that those factors which have influenced patterns of economic activity in the past and present will continue to do so in more or less the same manner in the future. Thus the major goals of time-series analysis are to isolate these influencing factors for forecasting purposes as well as for managerial planning and control. The classical multiplicative time-series model, which has been used for exploring the fluctuations among the component factors of a series in order to achieve the aforementioned goals, is developed. Such concepts as time-series decomposition, moving averages, exponential smoothing, and seasonal index utilization are discussed. In addition, the concept of MAD is introduced as a measure of the forecasting error when comparing linear, quadratic, exponential, and other forecasting models.

MULTIPLE CHOICE

1. The reference point against which all index numbers are computed is called

    (a) the price relative.   (c) the base period.
    (b) the commodity list.   (d) the aggregate value.

2. An aggregate price index represents

    (a) the changes in prices, over time, for an entire group of commodities.
    (b) the average of the changes in prices, over time, of each commodity in the index.
    (c) only perishable commodities.
    (d) None of the above.

3. In a "fixed" weight index the weights may be

    (a) established at a particular point in time.
    (b) developed as an average over several periods of time.
    (c) None of the above.
    (d) Both of the above.

4. The new Consumer Price Index for All Urban Consumers

    (a) includes persons living in institutions.
    (b) includes persons who are unemployed.
    (c) includes persons in the military service.
    (d) includes persons living on farms.

5. To use the CPI as a "deflator" of nominal wages:

    (a) Real Wages = (Nominal Wages $\div$ CPI) x 100.
    (b) Real Wages = (Nominal Wages x CPI) $\div$ 100.
    (c) Real Wages = (Nominal Wages + CPI) - 100.
    (d) Real Wages = (Nominal Wages - CPI) + 100.

6. In the decomposition of monthly time series data, the component which remains after all others are eliminated is:

    (a) the irregular movement.   (c) the seasonal variation.
    (b) the cyclical effect.   (d) the trend.

7. The method of least squares is used on time series data for

    (a) eliminating irregular movements.
    (b) deseasonalizing the data.
    (c) obtaining the trend equation.
    (d) exponentially smoothing a series.

8. Erratic, unsystematic fluctuations in a time series which are caused by such special unpredictable events as assassinations, floods, strikes, wars, etc. are called

208

(a) seasonal variations.   (c) secular trends.
(b) cyclical fluctuations.   (d) irregular movements.

9.   The persistent or overall tendency in a time series is called

      (a) exponential smoothing.   (c) irregular movements.
      (b) a moving average   (d) the trend.

10.   The annual multiplicative time series model does not possess a_____
      component.

      (a) irregular   (c) trend
      (b) cyclical   (d) seasonal

11.   Which of the following statements about the seasonal index in a time
      series are true?

      (a) It can be used to adjust a trend projection.
      (b) It can be used to help evaluate a particular month's results
          against previous results.
      (c) It can be used to eliminate the seasonal factors in the series.
      (d) All of the above.

12.   Which of the following statements about the method of exponential
      smoothing is not true?

      (a) It gives greater weight to more recent data.
      (b) It can be used for forecasting trend.
      (c) It can be used in lieu of moving averages to smooth a series.
      (d) It gives greater weight to past data.

EXAMPLES

I.   The following table presents the median salary schedules (in thousands
      of dollars) for the full-time instructional staff of a large, well-
      known university:

Position	Number* and Pay**	Year		
		1970	1974	1978
Professor	Q	111	100	92
	P	22.0	24.2	26.7
Associate Professor	Q	325	309	301
	P	17.5	19.7	22.3
Assistant Professor	Q	328	341	386
	P	12.2	14.9	18.3
Instructor	Q	232	221	197
	P	10.9	12.7	16.1

*Q=number of employees.
**P=median pay per annum in thousands of dollars .

Moreover, the following table presents the Consumer Price Index compiled for the particular geographic region in which the university is located:

Consumer Price (1967=100.0) Index	Year		
	1970	1974	1978
	118.1	145.2	197.5

(a) Using 1970 as the "base pay" year, construct the following indexes of salaries paid to the full-time instructional staff at this university for the year 1978:

(1) Simple Aggregate Index.
(2) "Fixed" Weights Aggregate Index (using 1974 as the weight period).

(b) Determine the percentage growth rate in "nominal" salaries paid to assistant professors over the 8-year period 1970 to 1978.

(c) Deflate the 1970 and 1978 figures by the Consumer Price Index for those years.

(d) Determine the percentage growth rate in "real" salaries paid to assistant professors over the 8-year period 1970 to 1978.

(e) Discuss how the purchasing power of assistant professors at this university has changed from 1970 to 1978.

SOLUTION

(a) Let the base year period 1970 be given the code 0. The index in the base year period is 100.0.
Let 1974 be given the code 1.
Let 1978 be given the code 2.

(1) Simple Aggregate Index

Position	$P_i^{(0)}$	$P_i^{(2)}$
Professors	22.0	26.7
Associate Professors	17.5	22.3
Assistant Professors	12.2	18.3
Instructors	10.9	16.1
Totals	62.6	**83.4**
Index	100.0	$\dfrac{83.4}{62.6}$ x 100 = 133.23

(2) Fixed Weight Aggregate Price Index

Position	$P_i^{(0)} Q_i^{(1)}$	$P_i^{(2)} Q_i^{(1)}$
Professors	22.0x100=2,200.0	26.7x100=2,670.0
Associate Professors	17.5x309=5,407.5	22.3x309=6,890.7
Assistant Professors	12.2x341=4,160.2	18.3x341=6,240.3
Instructors	10.9x221=2,408.9	16.1x221=3,558.1
Totals	14,176.6	19,359.1
Index	100.0	$\dfrac{19,359.1}{14,176.6}$ x 100 = 136.56

(b) Percentage growth rate in nominal salaries for assistant professors over 8-year period 1970 to 1978:

$$\frac{\$18.3 - \$12.2}{\$12.2} \times 100 = 50.0\%$$

(c) Using the Consumer Price Index to deflate nominal income:

$$\begin{array}{l} \text{Real salaries (in constant} \\ \text{1978 thousands of dollars)} \end{array} = \frac{\$18.3}{197.5} \times 100 = \$9.266,$$

$$\begin{array}{l} \text{Real salaries (in constant} \\ \text{1970 thousands of dollars)} \end{array} = \frac{\$12.2}{118.1} \times 100 = \$10.330.$$

(d) Percentage growth rate in real salaries for assistant professors over 8-year period 1970 to 1978:

$$\frac{\$9.266 - \$10.330}{\$10.330} \times 100 = -10.3\%.$$

(e) Over the 8-year period the salaries of assistant professors at this university have failed to keep pace with changes in prices, as measured by the Consumer Price Index. In this period, their purchasing power has diminished by 10.3%.

II.   The following data represent the annual sales revenues (in millions of dollars) over the 13-year period 1973 to 1985 for Ethel's Originals, a manufacturer of junior-sized dresses:

Year	1973	1974	1975	1976	1977	1978	1979	1980	1981	1982	1983	1984	1985
Sales Revenues	0.7	0.6	1.1	0.9	1.2	1.5	1.4	1.3	1.6	1.8	1.4	1.5	1.7

(a) Plot the data on a chart.

(b) Fit a least-squares trend line to the data and plot the line on the chart.

(c) What is the least-squares trend forecast for 1986?

(d) Using a smoothing coefficient of .25, exponentially smooth the series and plot the results on the chart.

(e) What is the exponentially smoothed forecast for the trend in 1986?

(f) Fit a 7-year moving average to the data and plot the result on the chart.

(g) Determine the cyclical-irregular relatives and plot the results on a separate chart.

(h) Convert the annual least-squares trend equation to a monthly trend equation and shift the origin to July 15, 1978.

(i) What is the least-squares trend projection for November 1986?

(j) If the seasonal index for November is .950, what would be the forecast for sales revenues in November 1986?

(k) Use the MAD to compare the annual least-squares trend equation to the exponential smoothing model.

SOLUTION

(a)

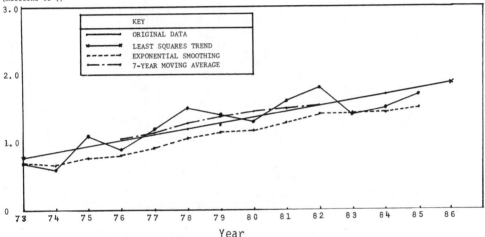

SALES REVENUES
(millions of $)

(b) Using the computer, the following results are obtained from a FORTRAN program:

$$n = 13 \quad \Sigma x_i = 0 \quad \Sigma y_i = 16.7 \quad \Sigma x_i^2 = 182.0 \quad \Sigma x_i y_i = 15.0$$

since n is odd

$$b_1 = \frac{\Sigma x_i y_i}{\Sigma x_i^2} = \frac{15.0}{182.0} \cong .082 \text{ and } b_0 = \bar{y} \cong 1.285$$

so that $\hat{y}_i = 1.285 + .082 x_i$

where origin = 1979 and x units = 1 year.

(c) The least-squares trend forecast for 1986 is:

$$1986 : \hat{y}_{14} = 1.285 + .082(7) \cong 1.86 \text{ millions of dollars.}$$

(d) To exponentially smooth a series we have

$$\varepsilon_i = Wy_i + (1-W)\varepsilon_{i-1}$$

where the smoothed value in the ith period, ε_i, is a function of the observed value in the ith period (y_i), the smoothed value from the previous period (ε_{i-1}), and the smoothing coefficient (W). Using a FORTRAN program, the following results are obtained:

Period = i	Year	y_i	ε_i
1	1973	0.70	0.70
2	1974	0.60	0.67
3	1975	1.10	0.78
4	1976	0.90	0.81
5	1977	1.20	0.91
6	1978	1.50	1.06
7	1979	1.40	1.14
8	1980	1.30	1.18
9	1981	1.60	1.29
10	1982	1.80	1.41
11	1983	1.40	1.41
12	1984	1.50	1.43
13	1985	1.70	1.50

(e) The exponentially smoothed trend forecast for 1986 is equivalent to the smoothed value for the previous period, 1985. Thus,

$$\hat{y}_{1986} = \varepsilon_{1985} = 1.50 \text{ millions of dollars.}$$

(f) Using a FORTRAN program, the following 7-year moving average is obtained:

Period = i	y_i	7-Year Moving Total	7-Year Moving Average
1	0.70	*.*	*.*
2	0.60	*.*	*.*
3	1.10	*.*	*.*
4	0.90	7.40	1.06
5	1.20	8.00	1.14
6	1.50	9.00	1.29
7	1.40	9.70	1.39
8	1.30	10.20	1.46
9	1.60	10.50	1.50
10	1.80	10.70	1.53
11	1.40	*.*	*.*
12	1.50	*.*	*.*
13	1.70	*.*	*.*

(g) Using a FORTRAN program, the cyclical-irregular relatives are
     determined as follows:

x_i	Year	y_i	$\hat{y}_i = b_0 + b_1 x_i$	$y_i / \hat{y}_i$
-6.0	1973	0.70	0.79	0.886
-5.0	1974	0.60	0.87	0.688
-4.0	1975	1.10	0.95	1.152
-3.0	1976	0.90	1.04	0.868
-2.0	1977	1.20	1.12	1.072
-1.0	1978	1.50	1.20	1.248
0.0	1979	1.40	1.28	1.090
1.0	1980	1.30	1.37	0.951
2.0	1981	1.60	1.45	1.104
3.0	1982	1.80	1.53	1.175
4.0	1983	1.40	1.61	0.867
5.0	1984	1.50	1.70	0.884
6.0	1985	1.70	1.78	0.956
7.0	1986	*.*	1.86	*.*
8.0	1987	*.*	1.94	*.*
9.0	1988	*.*	2.03	*.*

CYCLICAL--IRREGULAR RELATIVES

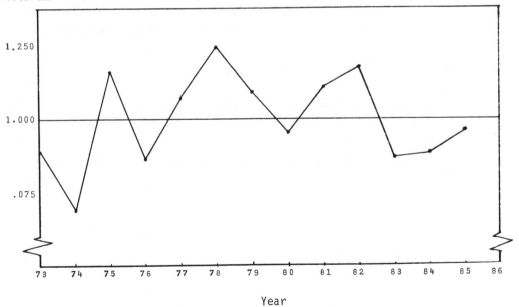

Year

(h) To convert the annual least-squares trend equation to a monthly trend equation we divide the intercept by 12 and the slope by 144. Thus,

$$\hat{y}_i = \frac{1.285}{12} + \frac{.082}{144} x_i = .1071 + .00057 x_i$$

where origin = June 30–July 1, 1979 and X units = 1 month.

To shift to the middle of the month, July, we have

$$\hat{y}_i = .1071 + .00057(x_i + 0.5)$$

so that

$$\hat{y}_i = .1074 + .00057 x_i$$

where origin = July 15, 1979 and X units = 1 month.

(i) To obtain the least-squares trend projection for November 1986, let $x_i = 88$, since the month of interest occurs 88 months after the origin month (July 1979). Thus,

$$\hat{y}_i = .1074 + (.00057)(88) = .1576 \text{ millions of dollars or}$$
$157,600.

(j) If the seasonal index for November is .950, the forecast of sales revenue in November 1986 is $\hat{y}_i \cdot$ seasonal index =

$$(.1576)(.950) = .1497 \text{ millions of dollars or } \$149,700.$$

(k) $\text{MAD} = \dfrac{\Sigma |y_i - \hat{y}_i|}{n}$

Linear Trend Model: MAD = 2.13/13 = 0.164
Exponential Smoothing Model: MAD = 2.57/12 = 0.214(Note:first year is excluded).

Historically, the linear trend model has fit the data better.

REVIEW PROBLEMS

I.   The following table presents the prices paid by typical families of four for selected nonfrozen breakfast juices purchased at super-markets in a large city:

Juice	Quantity* and Price**	Year		
		1972	1975	1978
Apple	Q	3.1	3.9	3.7
	P	.78	1.10	1.39
Orange	Q	4.5	4.2	4.8
	P	.53	.69	1.20
Pineapple	Q	2.4	2.8	2.7
	P	.61	.80	.92
Prune	Q	1.0	1.1	1.3
	P	.27	.39	.59

    *Q=in thousands of units.
    **P=in dollars per unit.

Moreover, the following table presents the Consumer Price Index for food and beverages compiled for the geographic region of interest:

Consumer Price (1967=100.0) Index	Year		
	1972	1975	1978
	121.7	163.3	202.5

(a) Using 1972 as the "base price" year, construct the following indexes of prices paid by typical families of four for selected nonfrozen breakfast juices for the year 1978:

(1) Simple Aggregate

(2) "Fixed" Weights (using 1975 as the weight period).

(b) Determine the percentage growth rate in "nominal" prices paid for apple juice over the 6-year period 1972 to 1978.

(c) Deflate the 1972 and 1978 figures by the Consumer Price Index for those years.

(d) Determine the percentage growth rate in "real" prices paid for apple juice over the 6-year period 1972 to 1978.

II.   The following data represent the sales revenues (in millions of dollars) over the 10-year period 1976 through 1985 for the Little Angela Corporation--the manufacturer of the famous Lovable Lori, Kuddly Kathy and Sweet Sharyn dolls and accessories:

Year	1976	1977	1978	1979	1980	1981	1982	1983	1984	1985
Sales Revenues	8.7	8.3	9.6	10.0	12.5	12.7	14.1	15.0	16.5	17.7

(a) Plot the data on a chart.

(b) Fit a least-squares trend line to the data and plot the line on the chart.

218

(c) What is the least-squares trend forecast for 1986?

(d) Using a smoothing coefficient of .40, exponentially smooth the series and plot the results on the chart.

(e) What is the exponentially smoothed forecast for the trend in 1986?

(f) Use the Holt-Winters forecasting method with U=0.3 and V=0.3. What is your forecast for the year 1986?

(g) Fit a second-order autoregressive model to the data and test for the significance of the second-order autoregressive parameter.
   If the model is appropriate, what is your forecast for the year 1986?

(h) Convert the annual least-squares trend equation to a monthly trend equation and shift the origin to July 15, 1976.

(i) What is the least-squares trend projection for July 1986 and for December 1986?

(j) If the seasonal index for July is .750 and if the seasonal index for December is 1.225, what would be the forecasts for sales revenue in July 1986 and in December 1986?

(k) Use the MAD to compare the annual least-squares trend equation to the exponential smoothing model.

SOLUTIONS TO REVIEW PROBLEMS

I. (a) Let the base year period 1972 be given the code 0.   The index in
        the base year period is 100.0.
        Let 1975 be given the code 1.
        Let 1978 be given the code 2.

        (1)Simple Aggregate Price Index:

$$I_{SA}^{(2)} = \frac{\Sigma P_i^{(2)}}{\Sigma P_i^{(0)}} \times 100 = 187.21.$$

        (2)Fixed Weight Aggregate Price Index:

$$I_{FWA}^{(2)} = \frac{\Sigma P_i^{(2)} Q_i^{(1)}}{\Sigma P_i^{(0)} Q_i^{(1)}} \times 100 = 188.18.$$

    (b) Percentage growth rate in nominal prices paid for apple juice:

$$\frac{\$1.39 - \$.78}{\$.78} \times 100 = 78.2\%.$$

    (c) Deflating nominal prices:

$$\text{Real Prices (in constant 1978 \$)} = \frac{\$1.39}{202.5} \times 100 = \$.69.$$

$$\text{Real Prices (in constant 1972 \$)} = \frac{\$.78}{121.7} \times 100 = \$.64.$$

    (d) Percentage growth rate in real prices paid for apple juice:

$$\frac{\$.69 - \$.64}{\$.64} \times 100 = 7.8\%.$$

II. (a)

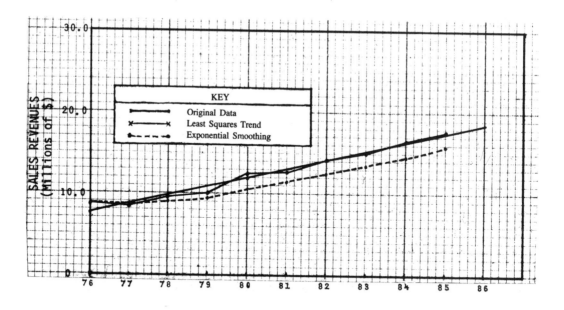

(b) n = 10. Since n is even, we have

$$b_1 = \frac{\Sigma x_i y_i - \dfrac{(\Sigma x_i)(\Sigma y_i)}{n}}{\Sigma x_i^2 - \dfrac{(\Sigma x_i)^2}{n}} = 1.0782$$

and

$$b_0 = \bar{y} - b_1\bar{x} = 7.6582$$

so that

$$\hat{y}_i = 7.6582 + 1.0782 x_i$$

where origin = 1976 and x units = 1 year.

(c) Least-squares trend forecast for 1986 is:

1986: $\hat{y}_{11} = 7.6582 + (1.0782)(10) \cong 18.44$ millions of dollars.

(d) Using an exponential smoothing coefficient $W = 0.40$, we have:

Period = i	Year	y_i	ε_i
1	1976	8.70	8.70
2	1977	8.30	8.54
3	1978	9.60	8.96
4	1979	10.00	9.38
5	1980	12.50	10.63
6	1981	12.70	11.46
7	1982	14.10	12.51
8	1983	15.00	13.51
9	1984	16.50	14.70
10	1985	17.70	15.90

(e) $\hat{y}_{1986} = \varepsilon_{1985} = 15.90$ millions of dollars.

(f) Using the Holt-Winters method:

Year	i	y_i	$U(\varepsilon_{i-1}+T_{i-1})+(1-U)y_i = \varepsilon_i)$	$VT_{i-1}+(1-V)(\varepsilon_i-\varepsilon_{i-1})=T_i$
1976	1	8.70	....	....
1977	2	8.30	8.30	-0.40
1978	3	9.60	0.3(8.30+(-0.4))+0.7(9.6 = 9.09	0.3(-0.4)+0.7(9.09-8.30) =0.43
1979	4	10.00	0.3(9.09+.43)+0.7(10.00) = 9.86	0.3(.43)+0.7(9.86-9.09) =0.67
1980	5	12.50	0.3(9.86+.67)+0.7(12.50) =11.91	0.3(.67)+0.7(11.91-9.86 =1.64
1981	6	12.70	0.3(11.91+1.64)+0.7(12.70)=12.96	0.3(1.64)+0.7(12.96-11.91)=1.23
1982	7	14.10	0.3(12.96+1.23)+0.7(14.10)=14.13	0.3(1.23)+0.7(14.13=12.96)=1.19
1983	8	15.00	0.3(14.13+1.19)+0.7(15.00)=15.10	0.3(1.19)+0.7(15.10=14.13)=1.04
1984	9	16.50	0.3(15.10+1.04)+0.7(16.50)=16.39	0.3(1.04)+0.7(16.39-15.10)=1.22
1985	10	17.70	0.3(16.39+1.22)+0.7(17.70)=17.67	0.3(1.22)+0.7(17.67-16.39)=1.26

Set $\varepsilon_2 = y_2 = 8.30$
and $T_2 = y_2 - y_1 = 8.30 - 8.70 = -0.4$.
Our smoothing constants are $U=0.3$ and $V=0.3$. These values are used to obtain the remaining ε_i and T_i values as shown in the above table.

To forecast $j=1$ year into the future we have

$$\hat{y}_{n+j} = \varepsilon_n + j(T_n)$$

1986: 1 year ahead $\hat{y}_{11} = \varepsilon_{10} + 1(T_{10})$

$$\hat{y}_{11} = 17.67 + 1(1.26)$$

$$\hat{y}_{11} = 18.93 \text{ millions of dollars.}$$

(g) Using Minitab we have:

```
-- READ C1
COLUMN          C1
COUNT           10
        8.7000          8.3000          9.6000          10.0000  .  .  .


-- NOTE 2ND ORDER MODEL

-- LAG 1 IN C1,PUT IN C2

-- LAG 2 IN C1,PUT IN C3

-- PRINT C1-C3
COLUMN          C1              C2              C3
COUNT           10              10              10
ROW
  1        8.7000*************************
  2        8.3000          8.7000*************
  3        9.6000          8.3000          8.7000
  4       10.0000          9.6000          8.3000
  5       12.5000         10.0000          9.6000
  6       12.7000         12.5000         10.0000
  7       14.1000         12.7000         12.5000
  8       15.0000         14.1000         12.7000
  9       16.5000         15.0000         14.1000
 10       17.7000         16.5000         15.0000


-- REGRESS C1 WITH 2 PREDICTORS C2 C3

    8 CASES USED
    2 CASES CONTAINED MISSING VALUES
```

The fitted second-order autoregressive model is

$$\hat{y}_i = 0.823 + 0.438 y_{i-1} + 0.641 y_{i-2}$$

To test for the significance of the second-order autoregressive parameter:

$H_0: \psi_2 = 0$

$H_1: \psi_2 \neq 0$

$\alpha = .05$ (2-tail)

$$Z \cong \frac{\hat{\psi}_2}{S_{\hat{\psi}_2}} = \frac{0.641}{0.281} = 2.28$$

Since $Z = 2.28 > 1.96$, we may reject H_0 and conclude that the second-order term significantly contributes to the overall model. Since the model is appropriate we may use it to forecast sales revenues for the year 1986:

$$\hat{y}_{n+j} = 0.823 + 0.438\,\hat{y}_{n+j-1} + 0.641\,\hat{y}_{n+j-2}$$

1986:1 year ahead $\hat{y}_{11} = 0.823 + 0.438(17.7) + 0.641(16.5) = 19.15$ millions of dollars.

(h) To convert the annual least-squares trend equation to a monthly trend equation and then shift the origin to July 15, 1976, we have:

$$\hat{y}_i = \frac{7.6582}{12} + \frac{1.0782}{144}\,x_i = .6382 + .00749x_i$$

so that

$$\hat{y}_i = .6382 + .00749(x_i + 0.5)$$

and thus

$$\hat{y}_i = .6419 + .00749x_i$$

where origin = July 15, 1976 and x units = 1 month.

(i) The least-squares trend projections for July 1986 and December 1986 are:

July 1986: $\hat{y}_i = .6419 + (.00749)(120) = 1.541$ millions of dollars.

December 1986: $\hat{y}_i = .6419 + (.00749)(125) = 1.578$ millions of dollars.

(j) To forecast sales revenues for July 1986 and December 1986 we have:

July 1986: $(1.541)(.750) = 1.156$ millions of dollars.

December 1986: $(1.578)(1.225) = 1.933$ millions of dollars.

(k) For the linear trend model, MAD $= \dfrac{4.26}{10} = 0.426$.

For the exponential smoothing model, MAD $= \dfrac{11.29}{9} = 1.254$ (Note: first year is excluded).

Historically, the linear trend model has fit the data better.

Appendix: Review of Arithmetic and Algebra

In writing this text, we realize that there are wide differences in the mathematical background of students taking a basic business statistics course. Some students may have taken various courses in calculus and matrix algebra, while many other students may not have taken any mathematics courses since high school. The emphasis in this text is on the concepts of statistical methods as they can be applied in business. No mathematical prerequisite beyond algebra is needed, since no formal mathematical proofs are derived. However, a proper foundation in basic arithmetic and algebraic skills will enable the student to focus upon understanding the concepts of statistics rather than the mechanics of computing results.

With this goal in mind, we should make clear that the object of this appendix is merely to review arithmetic and algebra for those students whose basic skills have become "rusty" over a period of time. If students need to actually learn arithmetic and algebra, then this brief review will probably not provide enough depth.

In order to assess one's arithmetic and algebraic skills, we would suggest that each student take the following quiz at the beginning of the semester:

PART I Fill in the correct answer.

1. $\dfrac{1}{2/3} =$

2. $.4^2 =$

3. $1 + \dfrac{2}{3} =$

4. $(\dfrac{1}{3})^4 =$

5. $\frac{1}{5}$ =   (in decimals)

6. $1 - (-.3)$ =

7. $4 \times .2 \times (-8)$ =

8. $(-\frac{1}{4}) \times (-\frac{2}{3})$ =

9. $\frac{1}{100} + \frac{1}{200}$ =

10. $\sqrt{16}$ =

PART II Select the correct answer.

1. If $a = bc$, then c =

    (a) ab
    (b) b/a
    (c) a/b
    (d) None of the above.

2. If $x + y = z$, then y =

    (a) z/x
    (b) z + x
    (c) z - x
    (d) None of the above.

3. $x^3 \cdot x^2$ =

    (a) x^5
    (b) x^6
    (c) x^1
    (d) None of the above.

4. x^0 =

    (a) x
    (b) 1
    (c) 0
    (d) None of the above.

5. $x(y - z)$ =

    (a) xy - xz
    (b) xy - z
    (c) (y - z)/x
    (d) None of the above.

6. $\frac{x + y}{z}$ =

    (a) (x/z) + y
    (b) (x/z) + (y/z)
    (c) x + (y/z)
    (d) None of the above.

7. $\frac{x}{y + z}$ =

    (a) (x/y) + (1/z)
    (b) (x/y) + (x/z)
    (c) (y + z)/x
    (d) None of the above.

8. If x=10, y=5. z=2, w=20

    then $\frac{xy - z^2}{w}$ =

    (a) 5   (c) 46
    (b) 2.3   (d) None of the above.

9. $\frac{8x^4}{4x^2}$ =

    (a) $2x^2$ (c) 2x
    (b) 2   (d) None of above.

10. $\sqrt{\frac{x}{y}}$ =

    (a) $\sqrt{y}/\sqrt{x}$ (c) $\sqrt{x}/\sqrt{y}$
    (b) $\sqrt{1}/\sqrt{xy}$ (d) None of above.

The answers to both parts of this quiz appear at the end of this appendix.

REVIEW OF ARITHMETIC AND ALGEBRAIC OPERATIONS

A. Symbols

Each of the four basic arithmetic operations--addition, subtraction, multiplication, and division--are indicated by an appropriate symbol:

+ add   x multiply

- subtract   ÷ divide

In addition to these operations, the following symbols are used to indicate equality or inequality:

= equals   ≠ not equal

≈ approximately equal to

> greater than   < less than

> or ≥ greater than or equal to

< or ≤ less than or equal to

B. Addition

The process of addition refers to the summation or accumulation of a set of numbers. In adding numbers together, there are two basic principles or laws; the commutative law and the associative law.

The commutative law states that the order in which numbers are added is irrelevant. This can be seen in the following two examples:

$$1 + 2 = 3 \qquad\qquad x + y = z$$

$$2 + 1 = 3 \qquad\qquad y + x = z$$

In each example, it did not matter which number was added first and which was added second, the result was the same.

The associative law of addition states that in adding several numbers, any subgrouping of the numbers can be added first, last, or in the middle. This can be seen in the following example:

(1) $2 + 3 + 6 + 7 + 4 + 1 = 23$

(2) $(5) + (6 + 7) + 4 + 1 = 23$

(3) $5 \;+\; 13 \;+\; 5 = 23$

(4) $5 + 6 + 7 + 4 + 1 \quad = 23$

In each of these cases the order in which the numbers have been added has no effect on the result.

C. Subtraction

The process of subtraction is the opposite or inverse of addition. The operation of subtracting 1 from 2 (2 - 1) means that one unit is to be <u>taken away</u> from two units, leaving a remainder of one unit. In contrast to addition, the commutative and associative laws to <u>not</u> hold for subtraction. Therefore, as indicated in the following examples, we have

8 - 4 = 4	but	4 - 8 = -4
3 - 6 = -3	but	6 - 3 = +3
8 - 3 - 2 = 3	but	3 - 2 - 8 = -7
9 - 4 - 2 = 3	but	2 - 4 - 9 = -11

In subtracting negative numbers, we must remember that subtracting a a negative number produces the same result as adding a positive number. Thus we have

4 - (-3) = +7	4 + 3 = 7
8 - (-10) = +18	8 + 10 = 18

D. Multiplication

The operation of multiplication actually is a short cut method of adding when the same number is to be added several times. For example, if 7 is to be added three times (7 + 7 + 7) we can equivalently multiply 7 by 3 to obtain a product of 21.

In multiplication, as in addition, the commutative laws and associative laws are in operation so that:

$$a \times b = b \times a$$
$$4 \times 5 = 5 \times 4 = 20$$
$$(2 \times 5) \times 6 = 10 \times 6 = 60$$

A third law of multiplication, the <u>distributive</u> law, applies to the multiplication of one number by the sum of several other numbers. Thus,

$$a (b + c) = ab + ac$$
$$2 (3 + 4) = 2 (7) = 2(3) + 2(4) = 14$$

Here the resulting product is the same regardless of whether b and c are summed and multiplied by a or a is multiplied by b and by c and the two products then added together. Furthermore, in multiplying negative numbers, we should remember that a negative number multiplied by a negative number equals a positive number. Thus,

$$(-a) \times (-b) = ab$$
$$(-5) \times (-4) = +20$$

E. Division

Just as subtraction is the opposite of addition, division is the opposite or inverse of multiplication. When we discussed multiplication, we viewed it as a shortcut to addition in certain situations. In a similar manner, division can be thought of in terms of subtraction. When we divide 20 by 4, we are actually determining the number of times that 4 can be subtracted from 20. However, in general, the number of times that one number can be divided by another does not have to be an exact integer value since there could be a remainder. For example, if 21 rather than 20 were divided by four, we would have an answer of 5 with a remainder of 1, or 5¼.

As in the case of subtraction, neither the commutative nor associative law of addition holds for division so that

$$a \div b \neq b \div a$$
$$9 \div 3 \neq 3 \div 9$$
$$6 \div (3 \div 2) = 4$$
$$(6 \div 3) \div 2 = 1$$

Moreover, the distributive law will only hold when the numbers to be added are contained in the numerator, not the demoninator. Thus,

$$\frac{a + b}{c} = \frac{a}{c} + \frac{b}{c} \quad \text{but} \quad \frac{a}{b + c} \neq \frac{a}{b} + \frac{a}{c}$$

For example,

$$\frac{6 + 9}{3} = \frac{6}{3} + \frac{9}{3} = 2 + 3 = 5$$

but

$$\frac{1}{2 + 3} = \frac{1}{5} \neq \frac{1}{2} + \frac{1}{3}$$

The final, important property of division is that if the numerator and denominator are both multiplied or divided by the same number, the resulting quotient will not be affected. Therefore, if we have

$$\frac{80}{40} = 2$$

then

$$\frac{5(80)}{5(40)} = \frac{400}{200} = 2$$

and

$$\frac{80 \div 5}{40 \div 5} = \frac{16}{8} = 2$$

F. Fractions

A fraction is a number that consists of a combination of whole numbers and/or parts of whole numbers. For instance, the fraction 1/6 consists only of a portion of a number, while the fraction 7/6 consists of the whole number 1 plus the faction 1/6. Each of the operations of addition, subtraction, multiplication, and division can be applied to fractions. When adding and subtracting fractions, one must obtain the lowest common denominator for each fraction prior to adding or subtracting them. Thus, in adding 1/3 + 1/5, the lowest common denominator is 15 so that we have 5/15 + 3/15 = 8/15. In subtracting 1/4 - 1/6, the same principle can be applied so that we would have a lowest common denominator of 12, producing a result of 3/12 - 2/12 = 1/12.

The operations of multiplication and division of fractions are not complicated by the lowest common denominator requirement of addition and subtraction. Thus, if a/b is multiplied by c/d we obtain

$$\frac{a \times c}{b \times d}$$

that is, the resulting numerator is the product of the numerators (a and c) while the denominator is the product of the two denominators (b and d). The resulting fraction can sometimes be reduced to a lower term by dividing numerator and denominator by a common factor. For example, taking 2/3 x 6/7 = 12/21 and dividing numerator and denominator by 3, produces a result of 4/7.

Division of fractions can be thought of as the inverse of multiplication, so that the divisor could be inverted and multiplied by the original fraction; that is

$$\frac{9}{5} \div \frac{1}{4} = \frac{9}{5} \times \frac{4}{1} = \frac{36}{5}$$

$$2 \div \frac{3}{7} = \frac{2}{1} \times \frac{7}{3} = \frac{14}{3}$$

Finally, the division of a fraction can be thought of as a way of converting the fraction to a decimal. For example, the fraction 2/5 can be converted to a decimal by simply dividing its numerator (2) by its denominator (5) to produce the decimal 0.40.

G. Exponents and Square Roots

The procedure of exponentiation provides a shortcut in writing out numerous multiplications. For example, if we have 2 x 2 x 2 x 2 x 2, then we may also write this as $2^5 = 32$. The 5 represents the exponent of the number 2, telling us that 2 is to be multiplied by itself five times.

There are several rules that can be applied for multiplying or dividing numbers that contain exponents.

Rule 1. If two numbers involving powers of the same number are multiplied, the product is that same number exponentiated to the sum of the powers $(x^a \cdot x^b = x^{a+b})$. Thus, $4^2 \cdot 4^3 = (4 \cdot 4)(4 \cdot 4 \cdot 4) = 4^5$

Rule 2. If we take the power of a number which is already taken to a power, the result will be the number exponentiated to the <u>product</u> of the two powers $(x^a)^b = x^{ab}$. For example,

$$(2^2)^3 = (2^2)(2^2)(2^2) = 2^6$$

Rule 3. If one number raised to a power is divided by the same number raised to a power, the quotient will be that number exponentiated to the difference of the powers $(x^a/x^b = x^{a-b})$. Thus,

$$\frac{3^5}{3^3} = \frac{3 \cdot 3 \cdot 3 \cdot 3 \cdot 3}{3 \cdot 3 \cdot 3 \cdot 1 \cdot 1} = 3^2$$

If the denominator has a higher power, the resulting quotient will be a negative power. Thus,

$$\frac{3^3}{3^5} = \frac{3 \cdot 3 \cdot 3 \cdot 1 \cdot 1}{3 \cdot 3 \cdot 3 \cdot 3 \cdot 3} = \frac{1 \cdot 1}{3 \cdot 3} = \frac{1}{3^2} = 3^{-2}$$

If the difference between the power of the numerator and denominator is 1, the result will be the actual number itself, so that $x^1 = x$. For example,

$$\frac{3^3}{3^2} = \frac{3 \cdot 3 \cdot 3}{3 \cdot 3 \cdot 1} = 3^1 = 3$$

If, however, there is no difference in the power of the number in the numerator and denominator, the result will be 1. Thus,

$$\frac{x^a}{x^a} = x^{a-a} = x^0 = 1$$

Therefore, any number exponentiated to the zero power will equal 1. For example,

$$\frac{3^3}{3^3} = \frac{3 \cdot 3 \cdot 3}{3 \cdot 3 \cdot 3} = 3^0 = 1$$

The square root represents a special power of a number, the 1/2 power. It indicates the value that when multiplied by itself will produce the original number. It is given by the symbol $\sqrt{}$ Thus, $\sqrt{x}$ represents the number which, when squared, produces the number x. For example, the square root of 25 ($\sqrt{25}$) is 5 since $5^2 = 25$.

Square roots can readily be obtained in two ways:

(a) by direct square root calculation
(b) by using an electronic calculator

The first way, direct calculation, usually involves tedious computations using long divisions. The second way, using an electronic calculator, requires us to choose a calculator that contains the square root function.

232

H. Equations

In statistics, all formulas are expressed as equations where one unknown value is a function of some other value. Therefore it is extremely useful that we know how to manipulate equations into various forms. The rules of addition, subtraction, multiplication, and division can be used to work with equations. For example, if we have the equation $x - 2 = 5$, we can solve for x by adding two to each side of the equation. Thus we would have $x - 2 + 2 = 5 + 2$ and, therefore, $x = 7$. If we had $x + y = z$, we could solve for x by subtracting y from both sides of the equation so that $x = z - y$. If we have the product of two variables equal to the third, such as $x \cdot y = z$, we can solve for x by dividing both sides of the equation by y. Thus, $x = z/y$. On the other hand, if $x/y = z$, we can solve for x by multiplying both sides of the equation by y. Hence x would equal yz. In summary, the various operations of addition, subtraction, multiplication and division can be applied to equations as long as the same operation is performed on each side of the equation-- thereby maintaining the equality.

ANSWERS TO QUIZ

	Part I				Part II		
1.	3/2	6.	1.30	1.	c	6.	b
2.	.16	7.	-6.4	2.	c	7.	d
3.	5/3	8.	+1/6	3.	a	8.	b
4.	1/81	9.	3/200	4.	b	9.	a
5.	0.20	10.	4	5.	a	10.	c

REFERENCE

W. L. Bashaw, Mathematics for Statistics; New York: John Wiley & Sons, 1969.

ANSWERS TO MULTIPLE CHOICE AND TRUE-FALSE QUESTIONS

Chapter 1   1.a 2.d 3.b 4.a 5.c 6.a 7.c

Chapter 2   1.c 2.d 3.b 4.b 5.b 6.d 7.b 8.d

Chapter 3   1.c 2.a 3.d 4.b 5.c 6.c 7.a 8.b 9.b

Chapter 4   1.a 2.b 3.d 4.d 5.c 6.a

Chapter 6   1.b 2.a 3.a 4.b 5.c 6.d

Chapter 7   1.d 2.b 3.b 4.a 5.c 6.b 7.c

Chapter 8   1.(a)F (b)F (c)T (d)T   2.d 3.d 4.b 5.b

Chapter 9   1.(a)T (b)F (c)T (d)T (e)F (f)T 2.d 3.b 4.c 5.b

Chapter 10   1.b 2.b 3.b 4.a 5.a 6.a 7.d 8.a 9.d

Chapter 11   1.c 2.a 3.c 4.c 5.b 6.a 7.a 8.b

Chapter 12   1.b 2.d 3.d 4.c

Chapter 13   1.a 2.b 3.d 4.a 5.b

Chapter 14   1.b 2.c 3.b 4.d 5.c 6.c

Chapter 15   1.d 2.d 3.a 4.c 5.d 6.b

Chapter 16   1.b 2.d 3.d 4.b 5.a 6.b 7.d 8.d 9.d

Chapter 17   1.b 2.a 3.b 4.d 5.c 6.c 7.a 8.b 9.b

Chapter 18   1.c 2.a 3.d 4.b 5.a 6.b 7.c 8.d 9.d 10.d 11.d 12.d

Please note that there are no multiple choice or true-false questions in Chapter 5.